Instructor's Manual

Basic Mathematics
for Electricity and Electronics

8th Edition

Bertrand B. Singer
Late Assistant Chairman
Mathematics Department
Samuel Gompers High School
New York, New York

Harry Forster
Electronics Department
Miami-Dade Community College
University of Miami
Miami, Florida

Mitchel E. Schultz
Electronics Department
Western Wisconsin Technical College
La Crosse, Wisconsin

 **Glencoe
McGraw-Hill**

New York, New York   Columbus, Ohio   Woodland Hills, California   Peoria, Illinois

Cover photos: (l) John Paul Endress/The Stock Market, (c) John Lund/The Stock Market (r) Doug Martin

Basic Mathematics for Electricity and Electronics   ISBN 0-02-805022-3
Workbook for Basic Mathematics for Electricity and Electronics   ISBN 0-02-805023-1
Instructor's Manual for Basic Mathematics for Electricity and Electronics   ISBN 0-02-805024-X

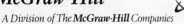

Glencoe/McGraw-Hill

A Division of The *McGraw-Hill* Companies

Instructor's Manual for Basic Mathematics for Electricity and Electronics

Send all inquiries to:
Glencoe/McGraw-Hill
936 Eastwind Drive
Westerville, OH 43081

ISBN 0-02-805024-X

Printed in the United States of America

1 2 3 4 5 6 7 8 9   047   07 06 05 04 03 02 01 00 99

Contents

Preface

The primary goal of our program is to help students develop the skills and competencies they will need to enter the workforce. In electricity and electronics, students must have a solid foundation in basic math skills and be able to apply those mathematical skills in order to achieve success at work.

The eighth edition of the *Instructor's Manual for Basic Mathematics for Electricity and Electronics* contains many new features. The manual now includes all of the student text answers and all of the new workbook answers. To help you use the new CD-ROM software, a user's guide is also included. Transparency masters of various figures from the student edition have been added for your convenience. The manual now features a new, more durable, 4-color soft cover.

New to the student edition are Learning Objectives that appear at the beginning of each chapter. Two new margin features are Calculator Hints, which describe calculator usage, and Student Success Hints, which advise students on how to study, ask for help, and prepare for tests. An Assessment page has been added to the end of each chapter to help students determine what they need to study before taking the chapter test. Also included are Internet Activities, which require students to go online to find solutions.

New to the program are a workbook and an instructor's CD-ROM. The workbook contains computational problems and/or applications for every job in the student text. The instructor's CD-ROM includes a Windows-based Test Generator and PowerPoint Slides for every chapter. A user's guide is included both on the software and in this instructor's manual.

Harry Forster, Jr.
Mitchel E. Schultz

Answers to Textbook Exercises

JOB 2-1 Page 14 **1.** 8 **2.** 8 **3.** 66 **4.** $\frac{1}{6}$ **5.** $\frac{1}{50}$ **6.** $\frac{1}{2}$ **7.** $45\frac{1}{3}$ **8.** 16 **9.** $25\frac{1}{2}$ ft **10.** $3\frac{3}{4}$ hp **11.** 90 V **12.** 7 Ω **13.** \$2.81 **14.** 228 kWh **15.** $37\frac{1}{2}$ h **16.** $94\frac{1}{2}$ W **17.** 36 lb **18.** 20 ft 3 in

JOB 2-2 Page 17 **1.** $\frac{1}{2}$ **2.** $\frac{1}{3}$ **3.** $\frac{1}{4}$ **4.** $\frac{1}{20}$ **5.** $\frac{3}{4}$ **6.** $\frac{5}{8}$ **7.** $\frac{1}{4}$ **8.** $\frac{1}{4}$ **9.** $\frac{1}{3}$ **10.** $\frac{1}{3}$ **11.** $\frac{3}{100}$ **12.** $\frac{1}{4}$ **13.** $\frac{3}{8}$ **14.** $\frac{2}{5}$ **15.** $\frac{7}{16}$ **16.** $\frac{1}{4}$ **17.** $\frac{1}{3}$ **18.** $\frac{1}{5}$ **19.** $\frac{3}{5}$ **20.** $\frac{7}{12}$ **21.** $\frac{2}{1}$ **22.** $\frac{9}{10}$ **23.** $\frac{49}{1}$ **24.** $\frac{1}{20}$ **25.** $\frac{2}{5}$ **26.** $\frac{3}{5}$ **27.** $\frac{3}{4}$

JOB 2-2 Page 19 **1.** $\frac{9}{4}$ **2.** $\frac{27}{8}$ **3.** $\frac{20}{9}$ **4.** $\frac{43}{8}$ **5.** $\frac{13}{10}$ **6.** $\frac{19}{4}$ **7.** $\frac{25}{6}$ **8.** $\frac{37}{10}$ **9.** $\frac{37}{8}$ **10.** $\frac{21}{2}$ **11.** $\frac{10}{3}$ **12.** $\frac{25}{12}$

JOB 2-2 Page 20 **1.** $1\frac{3}{4}$ **2.** $4\frac{1}{2}$ **3.** $4\frac{1}{3}$ **4.** $2\frac{2}{3}$ **5.** $3\frac{3}{4}$ **6.** $4\frac{3}{5}$ **7.** $1\frac{3}{5}$ **8.** $5\frac{3}{4}$ **9.** $3\frac{3}{10}$ **10.** $2\frac{4}{5}$ **11.** 10 **12.** $4\frac{3}{10}$ **13.** $9\frac{2}{3}$ **14.** $3\frac{1}{4}$ **15.** 16 **16.** $1\frac{7}{9}$ **17.** $3\frac{3}{5}$ **18.** 13 **19.** 12 **20.** $7\frac{3}{4}$ **21.** 7 **22.** $12\frac{2}{3}$ **23.** $1\frac{7}{10}$ **24.** $7\frac{3}{8}$ **25.** $5\frac{2}{9}$ **26.** $3\frac{1}{6}$ **27.** 12 **28.** $4\frac{3}{11}$ **29.** $12\frac{1}{4}$ **30.** $6\frac{3}{5}$

JOB 2-2 Page 22 **1.** 4 **2.** $\frac{2}{15}$ **3.** $\frac{3}{10}$ **4.** $\frac{3}{4}$ **5.** $2\frac{1}{2}$ **6.** $1\frac{3}{4}$ **7.** $\frac{1}{15}$ **8.** $1\frac{1}{2}$ **9.** 6 **10.** $1\frac{1}{2}$ A **11.** $5\frac{1}{4}$ hp **12.** 46 Ω **13.** $\frac{1}{2}$ hp **14.** 2 oz **15.** 3200 W **16.** Motors = 125 k VA, Lights = 225 k VA, Heat = 25 k VA **17.** $\frac{1}{3}$ **18.** $\frac{1}{4}$ **19.** $\frac{5}{7}$ **20.** $\frac{1}{3}$

JOB 2-2 Page 23 **1.** $\frac{2}{3}$ **2.** $\frac{7}{8}$ **3.** $9\frac{1}{2}$ **4.** $4\frac{1}{4}$ **5.** $\frac{1}{3}$ **6.** 4 **7.** 5 **8.** $8\frac{1}{10}$ **9.** $\frac{2}{3}$ **10.** 230 W **11.** $4\frac{1}{2}$ V **12.** 1275 W **13.** $7\frac{1}{8}$ h **14.** $\frac{1}{50}$ kW **15.** $67\frac{1}{2}$ ft **16.** 900 V **17.** $4\frac{1}{4}$ hp

JOB 2-3 Page 27 **1.** 55.8 V **2.** 117 V **3.** 44 V **4.** 111.3 V **5.** 117.6 V **6.** No; 0.27 V used **7.** 3.72 V **8.** 6.25 V **9.** 18.75 V **10.** 6.4 V **11.** 0.05 V **12.** 150 V **13.** $V_1 = 150$ V, $V_2 = 100$ V, $V_3 = 50$ V

JOB 2-4 Page 29 **1.** 5.55 A **2.** 0.015 25 μF **3.** 0.0378 in **4.** 0.35 A **5.** 2.6 V **6.** 1.185 in **7.** 65.75 V **8.** \$0.60 **9.** 0.004 Ω **10.** 12.55 **11.** 0.4 A **12.** (*a*) Four and three tenths, (*b*) Three hundred fifty-nine thousandths, (*c*) Forty-one hundredths **13.** 0.015 **14.** (*a*) 0.25, (*b*) 0.571, (*c*) 0.625, (*d*) 0.0625 **15.** 6.24 **16.** 1.1, 0.30, 0.050, 0.0070 **17.** 0.05 **18.** 2.25

JOB 2-5 Page 32 (top) **1.** 0.7 **2.** 0.29 **3.** 0.114 **4.** 0.3 **5.** 0.06 **6.** 0.009 **7.** 0.018 **8.** 0.003 **9.** 0.11 **10.** 0.4 **11.** 0.013 **12.** 0.74 **13.** 0.045 **14.** 0.316 **15.** 0.6 **16.** 0.23 **17.** 0.4, 0.16, 0.007 **18.** 0.28, 0.20, 0.107 **19.** 0.8, 0.06, 0.040 **20.** 0.8, 0.496, 0.02 **21.** 0.5, 0.18, 0.051 **22.** 0.90, 0.06, 0.018 **23.** 0.4, 0.236, 0.1228 **24.** 0.3, 0.05, 0.006 **25.** 0.19, 0.08, 0.004

JOB 2-5 Page 32 (bottom) **1.** 2.3 **2.** 18.05 **3.** 3.144 **4.** 1.17 **5.** 2.025 **6.** 7.35 **7.** 2.020 **8.** 3.09 **9.** 1.002 **10.** 62.90 **11.** 9.145 **12.** 3.027

JOB 2-5 Page 35 **1.** 0.25 **2.** 0.2 **3.** 0.625 **4.** 0.333 **5.** 0.4 **6.** 0.3 **7.** 0.15 **8.** 0.286 **9.** 0.875 **10.** 0.1875 **11.** 0.444 **12.** 0.867 **13.** 0.094 **14.** 0.84 **15.** 0.625 **16.** 0.563 **17.** 0.02 **18.** 0.005 **19.** 0.192 **20.** 0.141 **21.** 0.375 A **22.** 6.67

JOB 2-5 Page 36 **1.** 0.625 **2.** 0.218 75 **3.** 0.5625 **4.** 0.640 625 **5.** 2.25 **6.** 3.343 75 **7.** 1.140625 **8.** 4.75 **9.** $\frac{3}{8}$ **10.** $\frac{25}{32}$ **11.** $\frac{29}{64}$ **12.** $\frac{7}{8}$ **13.** $\frac{1}{32}$ **14.** $\frac{17}{32}$ **15.** $\frac{13}{32}$ **16.** $\frac{39}{64}$ **17.** $\frac{3}{4}$ **18.** $\frac{5}{8}$ **19.** $\frac{9}{64}$ **20.** $\frac{9}{16}$ **21.** $2\frac{13}{16}$ **22.** $3\frac{41}{64}$ **23.** $1\frac{27}{32}$ **24.** $\frac{15}{16}$ **25.** The lamp **26.** No

JOB 2-6 Page 39 **1.** 7.2 **2.** 4576 **3.** 3090 **4.** 0.45 **5.** 3700 **6.** 80 **7.** 0.6 **8.** 560 **9.** 2700 **10.** 15,000 **11.** 0.078 **12.** 7,800,000 **13.** 15,400 **14.** 45 **15.** 0.5 **16.** 60,000 **17.** 80 **18.** 900 **19.** 2340 **20.** 800

JOB 2-6 Page 40 **1.** 6.5 **2.** 7.5 **3.** 880 **4.** 0.32 **5.** 0.06 **6.** 1.78 **7.** 0.835 **8.** 0.000 55 **9.** 0.6538 **10.** 100 **11.** 0.000 45 **12.** 0.008 **13.** 0.0085 **14.** 0.000 007 **15.** 0.0286 **16.** 0.156 **17.** 0.002 **18.** 0.008 **19.** 0.0398 **20.** 0.6

JOB 2-6 Page 43 **1.** 350 mm **2.** 4.8 cm **3.** 24 cm **4.** 8 dm **5.** 360 dm **6.** 0.3 m **7.** 500 cm **8.** 3.25 m **9.** 2450 mm **10.** 6.5 m **11.** 12.5 cm **12.** 68 mm **13.** 42 dam **14.** 3.6 hm **15.** 750 hm **16.** 0.8 km **17.** 390 m **18.** 1 hm **19.** 20,000 m **20.** 3.498 km **21.** 150 dm **22.** 20 cm, 180 mm, 0.15 m **23.** 345.6 mm

JOB 2-7 Page 44 **1.** 13.492 **2.** 123.973 **3.** 22.832 **4.** 62.796 **5.** 11.967 **6.** \$39.55 **7.** 45.46 V **8.** 1.79 mm **9.** 0.1019 in **10.** 3.458 Ω

11. 0.0315 A   **12.** \$85.56   **13.** 25.38 mm
14. 0.1875 in   **15.** \$44.90

JOB 2-7   Page 45   **1.** 0.23   **2.** 1.18   **3.** 0.34
4. 0.046   **5.** 7.56   **6.** 0.623   **7.** 0.317   **8.** 0.517
9. 2.92   **10.** 0.48   **11.** 5.9   **12.** 0.33   **13.** 2.39
14. 5.6   **15.** 0.262   **16.** 5.94   **17.** 2.62   **18.** 3
19. 0.515   **20.** 55.1   **21.** (a) 0.304, (b) 1.106,
(c) 0.39, (d) 5.75, (e) 1.98   **22.** (a) 0.792, (b) 1.944
23. 0.1446 in   **24.** 8.29 Ω **25.** 0.43 mm
26. 218.85 V   **27.** 0.000 15 μF   **28.** 0.455 MHz

JOB 2-7   Page 47   **1.** 0.41   **2.** 69.28   **3.** 0.463
4. 0.081   **5.** 30.31   **6.** 35,903   **7.** 0.221   **8.** 0.0028
9. 0.0186   **10.** 0.000 082 5   **11.** 4.77   **12.** 80.4
13. 4.55 A   **14.** \$45.94   **15.** (a) 250 mA, (b) 25 mA,
(c) 2500 mA   **16.** \$21.38   **17.** 41.850 in
18. 56.52 Ω **19.** 69.6 A · h

JOB 2-7   Page 49   **1.** 13   **2.** 31.4   **3.** 161   **4.** 850
5. 4.7   **6.** 3700   **7.** 786   **8.** 6700   **9.** 2.32
10. 0.3 A   **11.** 200 ft   **12.** 19   **13.** 60.7
14. 0.207 Ω **15.** 40

JOB 2-7   Page 50   **1.** $A = 3.09$ in, $B = 2.8475$ in
2. 165.4 V   **3.** 0.082   **4.** 24 cm   **5.** (a) 735,
(b) 81,700,000, (c) 3.5, (d) 0.4, (e) 0.0007,
(f) 0.006 28, (g) 47.5, (h) 0.000 397   **6.** (a) \$52.45,
(b) 0.55   **7.** \$43.31   **8.** 12 A   **9.** 22.62 mm
10. \$28   **11.** 1.875 A   **12.** \$34.29   **13.** 163.9 W
14. 60.9 mm   **15.** No. 10

JOB 3-1   Page 54   **1.** 0.6 A   **2.** 300 Ω **3.** 111 V
4. 4 A   **5.** $kW = \dfrac{I \times V}{1000}$ **6.** 2 A   **7.** 25   **8.** 0.125 A
9. 11 A   **10.** 100 V

JOB 3-2   Page 58   **1.** $P = IV$ **2.** $V = 0.707\ V_{max}$
3. $Eff = \dfrac{P_o}{P_i}$ **4.** $R_T = R_1 + R_2 + R_3$ **5.** $X_C = \dfrac{159,000}{fC}$
6. $PF = R_T/Z$ **7.** $P = 2L + 2W$ **8.** $I_m = I - I_s$
9. $I_T = \dfrac{V_T}{R_1 + R_2}$ **10.** $R_s = R_m/(N - 1)$

JOB 3-2   Page 61   **1.** 14   **2.** 2   **3.** 20   **4.** 32
5. 18   **6.** 5   **7.** 6¼   **8.** 6   **9.** 7   **10.** 1   **11.** 135 ft^2
12. 5 A   **13.** 10 A   **14.** 0.4 kW   **15.** 140.4 Ω
16. 0.036 A   **17.** 20 Ω **18.** 56.52 Ω **19.** ¼ A
20. 68°   **21.** 72.6 Ω

JOB 3-3   Page 62   **1.** −\$3   **2.** −8°   **3.** +23°
4. +70°   **5.** +2 dB   **6.** −10°   **7.** −10 mph
8. +8 paces   **9.** −5 blocks   **10.** −20 ft   **11.** −4 V
12. −2 V

JOB 3-3   Page 65   **1.** +12   **2.** −11   **3.** +6   **4.** −7
5. −17   **6.** +19   **7.** +7   **8.** −12   **9.** −17
10. +32   **11.** −14   **12.** +22   **13.** +16   **14.** −70
15. −52   **16.** +3.4   **17.** +1.9   **18.** −9.8   **19.** +¼
20. +⅜   **21.** −⅚   **22.** −8⅛   **23.** −5¹¹⁄₁₆   **24.** +12¾
25. +3   **26.** +1   **27.** +7   **28.** −10   **29.** −25
30. −3   **31.** +0.5   **32.** −7.8   **33.** −2.9   **34.** +3.4

JOB 3-3   Page 66   (Multiplication)   **1.** +18
2. +12   **3.** −8   **4.** −18   **5.** +30   **6.** +6R
7. +18R   **8.** −12I   **9.** −10R   **10.** +15R
11. +10R   **12.** +72   **13.** 0   **14.** 0   **15.** −104
16. +150   **17.** −85R   **18.** −26I   **19.** −144R
20. −2   **21.** −6   **22.** −R   **23.** −2.4I   **24.** +10
25. −3R   **26.** +21.6   **27.** −14.72   **28.** +3.2I
29. −5.1R   **30.** −4.92R

JOB 3-3   Page 66   (Division)   **1.** +4   **2.** +6
3. −4   **4.** −8   **5.** +12   **6.** +4R   **7.** −6R   **8.** −4
9. −½   **10.** +6   **11.** +½   **12.** −⅓   **13.** 0   **14.** 0
15. −7   **16.** −20   **17.** −7½   **18.** −⅕   **19.** −3
20. −⁴⁄₇   **21.** +3⅕   **22.** −1.4   **23.** +130   **24.** −4
25. −2   **26.** −⅛   **27.** −3.2   **28.** +4   **29.** −62.5
30. +36

JOB 3-4   Page 67   **1.** 200   **2.** 360   **3.** 20 V
4. 65 Ω **5.** 0.000 000 5 F

JOB 3-5   Page 69   **1.** 3600 cmil   **2.** 268.8 in^3
3. 1024 ft   **4.** 539   **5.** 0.45 A   **6.** 21.6 hp
7. 0.032 V   **8.** 720 W   **9.** 132.25 W

JOB 3-6   Page 70   **1.** 7.2   **2.** 4576   **3.** 3090
4. 0.45   **5.** 3700   **6.** 8   **7.** 0.6   **8.** 560   **9.** 2700
10. 15,000   **11.** 0.078   **12.** 7,800,000   **13.** 15,400
14. 4500   **15.** 1   **16.** 60,000   **17.** 80   **18.** 900
19. 234,000   **20.** 50

JOB 3-6   Page 71   **1.** 65   **2.** 7.5   **3.** 880   **4.** 0.32
5. 0.06   **6.** 1.78   **7.** 0.835   **8.** 0.000 55   **9.** 0.6538
10. 100   **11.** 0.0045   **12.** 0.008   **13.** 0.0085
14. 0.000 007   **15.** 0.0286   **16.** 2   **17.** 0.000 02
18. 0.9

JOB 3-6   Page 72   **1.** 25   **2.** 2.5   **3.** 0.15   **4.** 0.005
5. 6.25   **6.** 1   **7.** 0.0025   **8.** 0.006   **9.** 0.007 54
10. 0.165

JOB 3-6   Page 73   **1.** 1920   **2.** 0.256   **3.** 850
4. 0.085   **5.** 7200   **6.** 9000   **7.** 0.000 045   **8.** 960
9. 88,000,000   **10.** 500   **11.** 3000   **12.** 20
13. 3,000,000   **14.** 5,000,000   **15.** 0.0006   **16.** 0.649

JOB 3-6   Page 74   **1.** 6×10^3 **2.** 5.7×10^3
3. 1.5×10^5 **4.** 5×10^5 **5.** 2.35×10^5
6. 7.35×10^6 **7.** 4.96×10^3 **8.** 6.25×10^4

9. 9.8×10^2 **10.** 1.75×10^2 **11.** 1.25×10
12. 7.30×10^3 **13.** 4.82×10 **14.** 1.26×10^4
15. 8.8×10^8 **16.** 5.4×10^4 **17.** 3.83×10^4
18. 8.02×10^3 **19.** 1.75×10^6 **20.** 2.4×10^6
21. 4.83×10^5

JOB 3-6 Page 75 1. 6×10^{-3} **2.** 7.5×10^{-3}
3. 3.5×10^{-3} **4.** 8×10^{-2} **5.** 4.56×10^{-1}
6. 3.57×10^{-2} **7.** 7.85 **8.** 1.2×10^{-7}
9. 9.65×10^{-2} **10.** 4.82×10^{-3} **11.** 5×10^{-1}
12. 3.74×10^{-4} **13.** 8.15×10^{-3}
14. 7.95×10^{-6} **15.** 7.25×10 **16.** 1.33×10^{-2}
17. 6×10^{-1} **18.** 3.2×10^{-2} **19.** 3.6×10^{-2}
20. 8×10^{-2}

JOB 3-6 Page 76 1. 5 **2.** 1.7×10^6
3. 6,400,000 or 6.4×10^6 **4.** 0.2
5. 30,000 or 3×10^4 **6.** 0.002 **7.** 120 **8.** 1.2
9. 0.03 **10.** 0.01 **11.** 5×10^{-7} **12.** 4.5 **13.** 960
14. 2×10^5 **15.** 628,000 or 6.28×10^5
16. (*a*) 9.42Ω, (*b*) $1.57 \times 10^6 \Omega$, (*c*) 1.57Ω

JOB 3-6 Page 78 1. 10^5 **2.** 10^{-2} **3.** 120 **4.** 10^6
5. 0.0002 **6.** 4×10^4 **7.** 2×10^{-7} **8.** 1 **9.** 8
10. 0.5 **11.** 5×10^{-3} **12.** 0.05 **13.** (*a*) 53Ω,
(*b*) 63Ω, (*c*) 3.18Ω

JOB 3-7 Page 82 1. 0.225 A **2.** 76 mV
3. $3,500,000 \Omega$ **4.** 5000 W **5.** 550,000 Hz
6. 700 kHz **7.** 0.07 MΩ **8.** 80 μF **9.** 65 mA
10. 6.5 kW **11.** 0.075 V **12.** 2,300,000 Hz
13. 0.006 A **14.** 7000 μF **15.** 0.0039 A
16. 75 kW **17.** 5000 pF **18.** 250 mA
19. 1,000,000 Hz **20.** $500,000 \Omega$ **21.** 8 mV
22. 4.5 mW **23.** 60 pF **24.** 150 mA
25. 0.000 000 15 F **26.** 0.125 V **27.** 8 kW
28. 4160 W **29.** 4 μA **30.** 600,000 Hz
31. 500,000 MHz **32.** 0.05 pF **33.** 0.015 GV
34. 0.25 nF

JOB 3-8 Page 83 1. 100 μV or 0.1 mV **2.** 10 V
3. 0.6 kW **4.** 0.2 mA **5.** 0.5 μA **6.** 59 mA
7. 215 kΩ **8.** 0.02 Ω **9.** 2625 pF **10.** 800Ω
11. 4×10^{-5} **12.** 81 W **13.** 14.1 V **14.** 6 V

JOB 3-9 Page 88 1. 5 **2.** 4 **3.** 6 **4.** 6 **5.** 9
6. 5¼ **7.** 13⅔ **8.** ¼ **9.** 5.85 **10.** 9½ **11.** 40
12. ⅕ **13.** 400 **14.** 1500 **15.** 200 **16.** 20
17. 800 **18.** 26,000 **19.** 390 **20.** 20 **21.** 1/16

JOB 3-9 Page 90 1. 2Ω **2.** 6 A **3.** 13Ω
4. 1000Ω **5.** 1½ A **6.** 440Ω **7.** 20 A **8.** 0.2 A
9. 25Ω **10.** 6 A **11.** 0.133Ω **12.** $15,000 \Omega$
13. 1200Ω **14.** 0.022 A **15.** 2.25 A **16.** 5.61Ω
17. 3.67 A **18.** 0.28 A **19.** 0.0015Ω **20.** 129.4Ω

21. 1.76Ω **22.** 400 V **23.** 0.002 A **24.** 5 A
25. 21.43Ω

JOB 3-11 Page 94 1. 110 V **2.** 11Ω **3.** Yes
4. 3 A **5.** 18 V **6.** 24 V **7.** 0.0007Ω **8.** 5 A
9. $10,000 \Omega$ **10.** 0.005Ω **11.** 0.004Ω
12. $12,000 \Omega$ **13.** 10 A **14.** 17.3 V **15.** 0.03 A
16. 86.5Ω **17.** 0.0081 A **18.** $300,000,000 \Omega$

JOB 4-1 Page 102 1. (*a*) 24 V, (*b*) 0.2 A, (*c*) 120Ω
2. (*a*) 6 V, (*b*) 3Ω **3.** (*a*) 42.9 V, (*b*) 0.3 A,
(*c*) 143Ω **4.** (*a*) 27.8 V, (*b*) 0.2 A, (*c*) 139Ω

JOB 4-2 Page 105 1. (*a*) 4 A, (*b*) 74 V, (*c*) 18.5Ω
2. (*a*) 6 A, (*b*) 120 V, (*c*) 20Ω **3.** (*a*) Dash = 2.5Ω,
tail = 5Ω, (*b*) 7.5Ω, (*c*) 0.8 A **4.** (*a*) 3.2 A, (*b*) 48 V,
(*c*) 15Ω **5.** 0.0088 A **6.** 5.1 V **7.** (*a*) 4.31 V,
(*b*) 7.7 V, (*c*) 12.01 V

JOB 4-3 Page 111 1. 550 V **2.** 42 V **3.** 4.8 V
4. (*a*) 2 A, (*b*) 160 V, (*c*) 80Ω **5.** 0.012 A
6. (*a*) 5 A, (*b*) 230 V, (*c*) 46Ω **7.** (*a*) 0.8 A, (*b*) 1.6 V,
(*c*) 2Ω **8.** (*a*) 204 V, (*b*) 4 A, (*c*) 51Ω **9.** 157.5 V

JOB 4-6 Page 118 1. 54 V **2.** 32.5 V **3.** 6 V
4. (*a*) 3 A, (*b*) 150 V, (*c*) 50Ω **5.** (*a*) 45, 75, 150 V,
(*b*) 270 V, (*c*) $18,000 \Omega$ **6.** (*a*) 0.25 A, (*b*) 110 V,
(*c*) 440Ω **7.** (*a*) 1.2 A, (*b*) 132 V, (*c*) 110 V
8. 160 V **9.** $V_T = 32$ V, $I_T = 0.4$ A, $I_1 = I_2 = I_3 =$
0.4 A, $R_1 = 20 \Omega$, $R_2 = 25 \Omega$, $R_3 = 35 \Omega$ **10.** $I_T = I_1$
$= I_2 = I_3 = 0.2$ A, $V_1 = 6$ V, $V_2 = 8$ V, $V_3 = 10$ V,
$R_T = 120 \Omega$

JOB 4-7 Page 119 1. 29 **2.** 26 **3.** 1.1 A **4.** 17.4
5. 7 **6.** 45 **7.** 12 **8.** 3 **9.** 25Ω **10.** 103.33

JOB 4-8 Page 121 1. 6 **2.** 8 **3.** 70 **4.** 50
5. 52 **6.** 1 **7.** 25 **8.** 4½ **9.** 7.3 **10.** 80
11. 28.2 **12.** 13 **13.** 5¼ **14.** 62.7 **15.** 6.1
16. 101.1 **17.** 56.1 **18.** 5.9 **19.** 120 **20.** 525
21. 73 **22.** 1.626 **23.** 0.000 08 **24.** 67 **25.** 1.45

JOB 4-8 Page 123 1. 17 **2.** 15 **3.** 22 **4.** 30
5. 5 **6.** 11.5 **7.** 12.5 **8.** 8.5 **9.** 79 **10.** 96
11. 10¾ **12.** 8¼ **13.** 15¼ **14.** 77¾ **15.** 80
16. 0.895 **17.** 0.099 **18.** 0.000 3 **19.** $21.83
20. 14 **21.** 172 **22.** 117 **23.** 17.05 **24.** 28
25. 109

JOB 4-8 Page 126 1. 11 **2.** 13 **3.** 6 **4.** 11
5. 10 **6.** 10 **7.** 12 **8.** 9 **9.** 8 **10.** 18 **11.** 1.54
12. 22 **13.** 10 **14.** 25 **15.** 11.5 **16.** 0.045
17. 0.021 **18.** 2.75 **19.** 11.48 **20.** 3.33 **21.** 1½
22. 6.27 **23.** 180 **24.** 11 **25.** 30 **26.** 70
27. 76.5 **28.** 103.5 **29.** 0.000 25 **30.** 0.003 85

JOB 4-9   Page 130   **1.** 25 Ω **2.** 14 Ω **3.** 8 Ω
4. 120 Ω **5.** 84 Ω **6.** 489 Ω **7.** 90 Ω **8.** 8.5 V
9. 202 V   **10.** 112.2 V   **11.** I_{max} = 11 A, I_{min} = 2 A
12. 0.012 Ω **13.** 0.025 Ω **14.** 250 Ω

JOB 4-10   Page 132   **1.** $I_T = I_1 = I_3$ = 2 A, V_T =
110 V, R_T = 55 Ω, R_1 = 12 Ω, V_2 = 60 V, V_3 = 26 V
2. 1 A   **3.** 12 Ω **4.** (a) I_T = 0.005 A, (b) V_1 = 5 V,
V_{CB} = 10 V, V_2 = 1.25 V, V_3 = 2.75 V   **5.** 28 Ω,
2.67 A, 74.8 V   **6.** 120 Ω **7.** (a) 2.2 A, (b) 10 Ω
8. 18 Ω **9.** 30 Ω **10.** 14,980 Ω

JOB 5-1   Page 140   **1.** (a) 5 A, (b) $V_1 = V_2 = V_3$ =
110 V, (c) 22 Ω **2.** (a) 105 A, (b) $V_c = V_m$ = 12 V,
(c) 0.114 Ω **3.** 4 A   **4.** (a) 8 A, (b) 14.6 Ω
5. 40 lamps; 30 lamps   **6.** (a) 10 A, (b) 110 V,
(c) 11 Ω **7.** 9.1 A; yes   **8.** (a) 1.8 A, (b) 110 V,
(c) 61.1 Ω **9.** 9.5 A, 1.26 Ω **10.** I_T = 8.37 A,
R_T = 13.1 Ω

JOB 5-2   Page 142   **1.** (a) 18 V, (b) I_1 = 6 A,
I_2 = 3 A, I_T = 9 A, (c) 2 Ω **2.** $V_1 = V_2 = V_3$ =
120 V, I_1 = 12 A, I_2 = 6 A, I_3 = 2 A, I_T = 20 A,
R_T = 6 Ω **3.** 2 A, 6 A; I_T = 12 A   **4.** (a) 20 V,
(b) 1.2 A, (c) 16.7 Ω **5.** (a) $V_T = V_1 = V_2 = V_3$ =
114 V, (b) I_2 = 6, I_3 = 2, I_T = 20 A, (c) R_1 = 9.5 Ω,
R_T = 5.7 Ω **6.** (a) 36, 18, 12 Ω, (b) $V_1 = V_2 = V_3$ =
7.2 V   **7.** (a) 30 Ω for 3 lamps; 15 Ω for fourth lamp,
(b) 0.25 A, (c) 1½ V, (d) 6 Ω **8.** $V_1 = V_2 = V_3 = V_T$
= 110 V, I_2 = 6.11 A, I_3 = 5 A, I_T = 12.42 A, R_T =
8.86 Ω **9.** I_T = 1.05 A, V_T = 6.8 V, R_T = 6.47 Ω
10. 7 A

JOB 5-3   Page 144   **1.** ¹⁷⁄₂₄ hp   **2.** ⅙   **3.** ⁹⁄₆₄ in
4. ¹⁵⁄₃₂   **5.** 22⅞ lb   **6.** ¹⁹⁄₃₀   **7.** 1¹³⁄₁₆   **8.** 2¹¹⁄₂₄   **9.** 1¹¹⁄₁₈
10. 1²⁷⁄₂₈   **11.** 2⅛   **12.** 4¹⁵⁄₁₆   **13.** 4¼   **14.** 2¹¹⁄₁₆
15. ¹⁄₆₀

JOB 5-4   Page 148   **1.** 1⅜   **2.** 2⁷⁄₄₈   **3.** 1¹¹⁄₂₄   **4.** 1¹¹⁄₁₈
5. ⅙   **6.** ¹¹⁄₁₈   **7.** ⅖   **8.** ¹⁴³⁄₃₁₅   **9.** ¹⁄₁₂₀   **10.** ³⁄₁₀₀
11. ⁵⁷⁄₆₄   **12.** 1³⁄₃₂   **13.** ³⁄₂₀   **14.** ¹⁹⁄₂₀₀₀   **15.** 1¹¹⁄₃₂
16. 7¹⁄₁₆   **17.** 15⁷⁄₁₆   **18.** 5⁷⁄₂₄   **19.** ¹⁵⁄₁₆   **20.** ⁷⁄₃₂ in
21. ¹¹⁄₆₀₀ S   **22.** 3⁸⁹⁄₁₀₀ MΩ **23.** 29²³⁄₂₄ ft

JOB 5-5   Page 152   **1.** ½   **2.** ½   **3.** ⅜   **4.** 4¼   **5.** ⁵⁄₁₆
6. ½   **7.** ¹⁄₁₂   **8.** 3⅙   **9.** ⅙   **10.** ¹⁄₁₀₀   **11.** ¹⁄₁₂   **12.** ¹⁄₉₀₀
13. ¹⁄₈₀   **14.** ¹⁄₁₅   **15.** ¹⁄₅₀₀   **16.** ¹⁄₆₀₀   **17.** 4¾   **18.** 7⅝
19. 7⅓   **20.** 2⅝   **21.** 5⁷⁄₁₆   **22.** 2¹⁄₂₄   **23.** ¹⁄₃₀₀   **24.** ³⁄₅₀₀₀
25. 76¾ ft   **26.** 4⅘ ft   **27.** ⁷⁄₃₂ in   **28.** 1⅞ in   **29.** ⅞ A

JOB 5-6   Page 153   **1.** 1800   **2.** 62.5   **3.** 2 A
4. 843   **5.** 6 V

JOB 5-7   Page 155   **1.** 24   **2.** 40   **3.** 12   **4.** 1.5
5. 1   **6.** 3.5   **7.** 2   **8.** 0.32   **9.** 8   **10.** 10

11. 6750   **12.** 549.9   **13.** 54   **14.** 550   **15.** 4000
16. 30.6   **17.** 30   **18.** 8.66   **19.** 93.97   **20.** 220

JOB 5-7   Page 157   **1.** 2   **2.** 6   **3.** 4   **4.** ⅔   **5.** 3⅓
6. 1.6   **7.** 15   **8.** 1.75   **9.** 15   **10.** 1½   **11.** 1.2
12. 3⅓   **13.** 10   **14.** 13⅓   **15.** 3½   **16.** 0.25
17. 7.8   **18.** 267   **19.** 315   **20.** 500   **21.** 120 turns
22. 9 V   **23.** 33⅓   **24.** 8 A   **25.** 60 Ω **26.** 269 Ω
27. 500 lb   **28.** 160 ft   **29.** 1.02 Ω **30.** 0.117 μF

JOB 5-7   Page 159   **1.** 6   **2.** 16   **3.** 80   **4.** 24
5. 51   **6.** 22   **7.** 27   **8.** 6   **9.** 25   **10.** 3   **11.** 10
12. 0.8   **13.** 1.44   **14.** 2.64   **15.** 5⅓   **16.** 1
17. 0.1   **18.** 0.0125   **19.** 1.84   **20.** 0.2

JOB 5-8   Page 162   **1.** 1.5 Ω **2.** 10 Ω **3.** 1.64 Ω
4. 13.6 Ω **5.** 1.9 Ω **6.** 2 Ω **7.** 2.5 Ω **8.** 62.5 Ω
9. R_A = 12.4 Ω, R_B = 11.25 Ω, R_C = 9.47 Ω
10. 462 Ω **11.** 60 Ω **12.** 900 Ω **13.** 1200 Ω
14. 400 Ω **15.** 20 Ω

JOB 5-8   Page 164   **1.** 50 Ω **2.** 16 Ω **3.** 0.75 Ω
4. 40 Ω **5.** (a) 7.33 Ω, (b) 45 A

JOB 5-8   Page 165   **1.** 20 Ω **2.** 15 Ω **3.** 24 Ω
4. 9 Ω **5.** 7143 Ω **6.** 16 Ω **7.** 3.53 kΩ
8. 1636 Ω **9.** 28.6 Ω **10.** 11,490 Ω

JOB 5-9   Page 166   **1.** 40 V   **2.** 122.7 V   **3.** 4.8 V
4. 4 V   **5.** 14.4 V   **6.** 0.01 V   **7.** 18.5 V   **8.** 17.1 V
9. 4.8 V

JOB 5-10   Page 171   **1.** $I_1 = I_2$ = 4 A (The current
in a circuit divides equally between equal parallel
branches.)   **2.** 5.4 A, 3.6 A   **3.** V_T = 6 V,
$I_1 = I_2$ = 4 A   **4.** I_G = 0.008 A, I_s = 0.192 A   **5.** 9 A,
6 A, 4.5 A   **6.** 12 A, 8 A, 6 A   **7.** I_2 = 0.024 A,
I_1 = 0.006 A   **8.** 0.071 A   **9.** (a) 2.14 Ω, (b) 28 V,
(c) $V_1 = V_2 = V_3$ = 28 V, (d) I_1 = 5.6 A, I_2 = 4 A,
I_3 = 3.5 A   **10.** I_1 = 0.0006 A, I_2 = 0.0024 A

JOB 5-11   Page 173   **1.** (a) 5.75 A, (b) 110 V,
(c) 19.1 Ω **2.** (a) 12 V, (b) R_s = 120 Ω, R_c = 60 Ω,
(c) 0.55 A, (d) 21.8 Ω **3.** I_T = 47 A, R_T = 9.36 Ω,
$V_1 = V_2 = V_3$ = 440 V, I_2 = 22 A, R_1 = 44 Ω, R_3 =
29.3 Ω **4.** $V_1 = V_2 = V_3$ = 32 V, I_1 = 3.2 A, I_2 = 2 A,
I_T = 6 A, R_3 = 40 Ω, R_T = 5.33 Ω **5.** 26.7 Ω
6. 1430 Ω **7.** (a) 10 Ω, (b) 8 Ω, (d) Series, (e) 18 Ω,
(f) 20 A   **8.** 19.2 Ω **9.** 600 Ω **10.** 30 Ω **11.** 85.7 Ω
12. 120 Ω **13.** (a) 2550 Ω, (b) 102 V
14. 12 A, 8 A, 6 A

JOB 6-2   Page 181   **1.** R_T = 24 Ω, I_T = 5 A, $I_1 = I_2$
= 3 A, I_3 = 2 A, V_1 = 30 V, V_2 = 90 V, V_3 = 120 V
2. R_T = 26.7 Ω, I_T = 9 A   **3.** R_T = 60 Ω, I_T = 2 A
4. R_T = 3 Ω, I_T = 2 A, $I_2 = I_1$ = 1.5 A, $I_3 = I_4$ =

4

0.5 A, $V_1 = 4.5$ V, $V_2 = 1.5$ V, $V_3 = 4$ V, $V_4 = 2$ V
5. (a) 12,000 Ω, (b) 0.03 A, (c) 360 V, (d) 0.012 A, (e) 0.018 A, (f) 54 V, (g) 306 V **6.** (a) 5000 Ω, (b) 7500 Ω, (c) 4286 Ω **7.** 8 Ω **8.** $R_T = 5$ Ω

JOB 6-3 Page 193 1. $I_T = 10$ A, $I_1 = 10$ A, $I_2 = 7.5$ A, $I_3 = 2.5$ A, $R_T = 13$ Ω, $V_1 = 100$ V **2.** $R_T = 10$ Ω, $I_T = 10$ A, $I_1 = 10$ A, $V_1 = 40$ V, $I_2 = 6$ A, $I_3 = 3$ A, $I_4 = 1$ A **3.** 0.5 A **4.** (a) $R_T = 20$ Ω, (b) $I_T = 6$ A, (c) $I_1 = I_6 = 6$ A, $I_2 = I_3 = I_4 = I_5 = 3$ A, (d) $V_1 = 30$ V, $V_2 = 3$ V, $V_3 = 9$ V, $V_4 = 18$ V, $V_5 = 30$ V, $V_6 = 60$ V **5.** 10 mA **6.** (a) $R_T = 200$ Ω, (b) $I_T = 2$ A, (c) $I_1 = 2$ A, $I_2 = 1.8$ A, $I_3 = 0.9$ A, $I_4 = 0.9$ A, $I_5 = 0.9$ A, $I_6 = 1.8$ A, $I_7 = 2$ A, $I_8 = 0.2$ A, $I_9 = 0.9$ A, (d) $V_1 = 100$ V, $V_2 = 45$ V, $V_3 = 7.2$ V, $V_4 = 1.8$ V, $V_5 = 9$ V, $V_6 = 27$ V, $V_7 = 210$ V, $V_8 = 90$ V, $V_9 = 18$ V **7.** $R_T = 30$ Ω **8.** 64.9 Ω **9.** (a) 60 kΩ, (b) 90 kΩ **10.** 18 Ω **11.** $R_T = 25$ Ω **12.** 24 Ω

JOB 6-4 Page 201 1. $V_1 = 2.4$ V, $V_L = 114.6$ V **2.** 220 V **3.** 0.25 Ω **4.** 9.62 V **5.** 6.048 V, No. 14 **6.** $V_1 = 3.7$ V, $V_L = 113.3$ V **7.** 113.3 V **8.** (a) 16.5 Ω, (b) 7.09 A, (c) 114.1 V

JOB 6-5 Page 205 1. (a) $V_1 = 15.2$ V, $V_2 = 4.8$ V, (b) 101.8 V, (c) 97 V **2.** (a) $V_1 = 7.2$ V, $V_2 = 3.6$ V, (b) 107.8 V, (c) 104.2 V **3.** $V_A = 112$ V, $V_B = 109.6$ V **4.** 112.2 V **5.** $V_G = 126.4$ V, $V_B = 111.1$ V **6.** $V_B = 110.8$ V, $I_A = 7$ A **7.** 125.8 V **8.** (a) 115.2 V, (b) 113.4 V **9.** $V_{M1} = 109$ V, $V_{M2} = 99$ V

JOB 7-1 Page 215 1. 480 W **2.** 17.02 kW **3.** 22 W **4.** 16.8 W **5.** 374 W **6.** 110 W **7.** 2.2 W **8.** 0.06 W **9.** 2.3 W **10.** 40 W **11.** 900 W **12.** 4.25 kW **13.** 1 W **14.** 1076 W **15.** 2508 W **16.** 200 W, 3000 W

JOB 7-2 Page 217 1. 11.2 W **2.** 11.2 W **3.** Yes. (0.135 W developed) **4.** 868 W **5.** 58.8 W **6.** 1930 W **7.** 2246 W **8.** (a) 10 A, (b) $P_1 = 640$ W, $P_2 = 960$ W, $P_3 = 160$ W, $P_4 = 240$ W, (c) $P_T = 2000$ W **9.** $I_T = 1$ A, $P_1 = 2$ W, $P_2 = 0.64$ W, $P_3 = 3.84$ W, $P_4 = 19.2$ W, $P_5 = 1.6$ W, $P_6 = 3$ W, $P_T = 13$ W

JOB 7-3 Page 218 1. 5 A **2.** 4 A **3.** 50 A **4.** 33.3 V **5.** 1.2 W **6.** 12.5 A **7.** 0.5 A **8.** 0.1 A, 0.1 A **9.** 5.45 A **10.** 56.8 A **11.** 20 A

JOB 7-4 Page 220 1. 720 W **2.** 220 W **3.** 6.25 W, 13 W **4.** 200 W **5.** 0.006 W **6.** 0.4 W **7.** 3361 W **8.** 0.9 W **9.** 661 W **10.** 0.055 W **11.** (a) 60 Ω, (b) 2 A, (c) 240 W **12.** (a) $I_T = 2$ A, (b) $P_1 = 88$ W, $P_2 = 4.5$ W, $P_3 = 17.5$ W, $P_4 = 20$ W, $P_5 = 126$ W, $P_6 = 120$ W, (c) $P_T = 376$ W **13.** (a) 100 Ω, (b) 2 A, (c) 400 W

JOB 7-5 Page 223 1. 10^{10} **2.** 10^{-8} **3.** 9×10^6 **4.** 25×10^{-6} **5.** 10^{10} **6.** 10^8 **7.** 64×10^6 **8.** 225×10^6 **9.** 121×10^4 **10.** 49×10^{-6} **11.** 625×10^{-10} **12.** 225×10^{-6} **13.** 2.25×10^6 **14.** 26×10^{-8} **15.** 1.44×10^{-6}

JOB 7-6 Page 225 1. 2.25 kW **2.** 0.81 W **3.** 132.3 W **4.** 25 W **5.** 6.5 W **6.** 807 W **7.** 6.36 A; 16.2 W **8.** 5.4 W **9.** 11.1 W; 28.9 W **10.** $V_T = 20$ V, $V_1 = V_2 = 20$ V, $P_1 = 26.7$ W, $P_2 = 13.3$ W

JOB 7-7 Page 226 1. 8 **2.** 13 **3.** 4.2 **4.** 59 **5.** 112 **6.** 7.6 **7.** 3.74 **8.** 23.8 **9.** 276.5 **10.** 5.48 **11.** 0.807 **12.** 932.6

JOB 7-8 Page 233 1. 59 **2.** 4.2 **3.** 3.9 **4.** 112 **5.** 137 **6.** 12.3 **7.** 6.32 **8.** 16.34 **9.** 8.06 **10.** 7.34

JOB 7-9 Page 236 1. 10^4 **2.** 10^{-3} or 0.001 **3.** $4 \times 10^2 = 400$ **4.** 3×10^{-3} or 0.003 **5.** $4 \times 10^2 = 400$ **6.** 0.08 **7.** 0.005 **8.** 40 **9.** 60 **10.** 4.47×10^2 or 447 **11.** $6.32 \times 10^2 = 632$ **12.** 2.45×10^{-2} or 0.0245 **13.** 4 **14.** 0.5×10^4 or 5000 **15.** $2 \times 10^2 = 200$ **16.** 21×10^{-4} or 0.0021 **17.** $1.732 \times 10^3 = 1732$ **18.** 2.53×10^{-2} or 0.0253 **19.** 12×10^3 **20.** 9×10^3 or 9000 **21.** 1.5×10^{-2} **22.** 25×10^{-7} **23.** 250 **24.** 70

JOB 7-10 Page 238 1. 10 A **2.** 6 V **3.** 2 A **4.** 0.14 A **5.** 20 V **6.** 6050 Ω **7.** 144 Ω **8.** 110 V **9.** 38.7 A **10.** 0.05 A

JOB 7-11 Page 240 1. 660 W **2.** 2200 W **3.** 550 W **4.** 2.27 A **5.** 43.2 W **6.** 0.9 W **7.** 6.25 V **8.** 40 Ω **9.** (a) $R_T = 16.8$ Ω, (b) $P_T = 6.05$ W **10.** 550 W **11.** 12.3 W **12.** 12.2 V **13.** 90 Ω **14.** 0.063 A **15.** $I_l = 20$ A, $V_L = 110$ V, $P_L = 2200$ V, No. = 44 lamps **16.** (a) 116.5 V, (b) 112.5 W, (c) 46.75 W, (d) 757.25 W **17.** (a) $R_T = 200$ Ω, (b) $I_T = 0.5$ A, (c) $P_T = 50$ W

JOB 8-1 Page 245 1. $8x$ **2.** $2y$ **3.** $6R$ **4.** $7I$ **5.** $12x$ **6.** $11y$ **7.** $5x$ **8.** $3.7R$ **9.** $4.4R$ **10.** $5.7I$ **11.** $3.5x$ **12.** $\frac{3}{4}y$ **13.** $\frac{5}{6}T$ **14.** $0.8x$ **15.** $9R$ **16.** $8.2I$ **17.** $7.5x$ **18.** $5.4x$ **19.** $4.5x$ **20.** $0.6y$ **21.** $6.6R$ **22.** $6x$ **23.** $2\frac{7}{8}x$ **24.** $1.7x$ **25.** $3x$ **26.** $2\frac{5}{8}y$ **27.** $1.12x$

JOB 8-2 Page 247 1. $10R + 7I$ **2.** $2R + 7I$ **3.** $2x + 9$ **4.** $7x + y$ **5.** $6R + 8$ **6.** $2I + 4$ **7.** $3R + 60$ **8.** $10I + 12$ **9.** $6x + 5y$ **10.** $6.5R + 2I$ **11.** $0.9I + 1.9R$ **12.** $5I + 35$ **13.** $8I_1 + 10I_2$ **14.** $6I_2 + 2.5I_1$ **15.** $4x + 5y + 10$

16. $2.1I_1 + 60$ **17.** $1.2I_2 + 2$ **18.** $7.3R + 10$
19. $2.4 + 3.4I$ **20.** $7.7R + 16.8$ **21.** $6x + 55$
22. $47.6 + 3.5y$ **23.** $0.45R\,\text{V} + 25\,\text{V}$
24. $7I_1 + 3I_2$ **25.** $19I_3 + 3I_2$ **26.** $7I_1 + 19I_3$

JOB 8-3 Page 252 **1.** 7 **2.** 7 **3.** 5 **4.** 6 **5.** 5
6. 30 **7.** 5 **8.** 10 **9.** 12 **10.** 36 **11.** 5 **12.** 6
13. $5\frac{1}{3}$ **14.** $\frac{1}{5}$ **15.** 200 **16.** 18 **17.** 30 **18.** $9\frac{1}{2}$
19. 70 **20.** 20 **21.** 5 **22.** 7 **23.** 0.8 **24.** 19.6
25. 5 **26.** 7 **27.** 2 **28.** $\frac{1}{2}$ **29.** $24\frac{1}{2}$ **30.** 2 **31.** 7
32. 10 **33.** 3 **34.** 3 **35.** 6 **36.** 6 **37.** 6 **38.** 0
39. $\frac{1}{4}$ **40.** 0.7 **41.** 0.7 **42.** 6 **43.** $6\frac{2}{3}$ **44.** 13
45. $10\frac{1}{5}$ **46.** $\frac{3}{4}$ **47.** 2 **48.** 2 **49.** 40 **50.** 5
51. 6 in, 3 in, 12 in **52.** $A = 4, B = 12, C = 16$
53. $A = 13, B = 0.4, C = 21.6$ **54.** $A = 8, B = 5,$
$C = 8$ **55.** $A = 32, B = 16, C = 8$ **56.** 24
57. (a) $2R + 150 = 200$, (b) $R = 25\,\Omega$ **58.** 1.25 in
59. Motor = 4 A, Lamp = 2 A, Iron = 7 A
60. $R_1 = 10\,\text{k}\Omega, R_2 = 30\,\text{k}\Omega, R_3 = 60\,\text{k}\Omega$
61. $V_1 = 30\,\text{V}, V_2 = 60\,\text{V}, V_3 = 30\,\text{V}$

JOB 8-4 Page 255 **1.** 10 **2.** 15 **3.** 30 **4.** 45
5. 166. 21 **7.** 15 **8.** 10 **9.** 10 **10.** 8 **11.** 13.2
12. 8 **13.** 3 **14.** 50 **15.** 28 **16.** 3 **17.** 12
18. 6 **19.** $12\frac{5}{6}$ ft **20.** Lamp = 1 A, Coffee = 5 A,
Toaster = 6 A

JOB 8-5 Page 258 **1.** $-2x + 7$ **2.** $9 - 6y$
3. $-4I_1 - 2I_2$ **4.** $3x - 7$ **5.** $-2x - 4y$
6. $5 - 9I_2$ **7.** $-3x - 7$ **8.** $-2x - 5y + 7$
9. $-20 - 2x$ **10.** $3x - 4y - 2$

JOB 8-6 Page 260 **1.** 2 **2.** 5 **3.** 9 **4.** 2 **5.** 4
6. 4 **7.** 10 **8.** 12 **9.** 5 **10.** 19 **11.** 7 **12.** $\frac{1}{2}$
13. $\frac{1}{3}$ **14.** 13 **15.** 5 **16.** 1.3 **17.** 4 **18.** 8 **19.** 9
20. 16 **21.** 7 **22.** 6 **23.** 8 **24.** 4 **25.** 5 **26.** 12
27. $\frac{1}{3}$ **28.** $\frac{1}{2}$ **29.** 2.1 **30.** 6

JOB 8-7 Page 261 **1.** -8 **2.** -12 **3.** -5 **4.** -7
5. $-\frac{1}{2}$ **6.** $-\frac{1}{2}$ **7.** -8 **8.** -10 **9.** $+7$ **10.** $+8$
11. -4 **12.** -4 **13.** -1 **14.** -7 **15.** -5
16. -8 **17.** -11 **18.** $+7$ **19.** -3 **20.** -50
21. -2 **22.** -130 **23.** -7 **24.** -0.71

JOB 8-8 Page 264 **1.** $6 - 8x$ **2.** $15x - 18$
3. $-3x + 12$ **4.** $5x - 12$ **5.** $3x - 5$ **6.** $y + 3$
7. $6I - 24$ **8.** $R - 1$ **9.** $1 - 2R$ **10.** $3 - 3x$
11. $29 - 3x$ **12.** $75 - 3I_1$ **13.** $20 + 2I_1 + 2I_2$
14. $6 + 4I_2$ **15.** $7R - 12$ **16.** $3x - 10$
17. $5 - 2R$ **18.** $2x - 8$ **19.** $3I_1 + I_2 - 24$
20. $x + 19$

JOB 8-9 Page 266 **1.** 1 **2.** 5 **3.** -2 **4.** 1 **5.** 2
6. 2 **7.** -3 **8.** 2 **9.** 3 **10.** 14 **11.** -1 **12.** -6
13. 3 **14.** 5 **15.** -4 **16.** 5 **17.** 7 **18.** 1 **19.** 4
20. 6 **21.** -21 **22.** 4 **23.** $\frac{1}{2}$ **24.** $3\frac{2}{3}$ **25.** 3

26. 4 **27.** $5\frac{1}{2}$ **28.** 3 **29.** 1.1 **30.** 1 **31.** 25
32. $R_1 = 20\,\Omega$ **33.** $48\,\Omega$ **34.** $68°$ **35.** 650 W
36. 0.98

JOB 8-10 Page 269 **1.** 2 **2.** 2 **3.** 40 **4.** 12
5. 30 **6.** 6 **7.** 8 **8.** 1 **9.** 7 **10.** 20 **11.** 6
12. 240 **13.** 300 **14.** 30 **15.** 10 **16.** 6 **17.** 2
18. 500 **19.** $17\frac{1}{2}$ **20.** 2 **21.** 108 **22.** 48

JOB 8-11 Page 275 **1.** $x - 3, y = 2$ **2.** $x = 5, y = 1$
3. $x - 5, y = 2$ **4.** $x = 3, y = -2$ **5.** $I_1 = 6, I_2 = 2$
6. $x = 4, y = 4$ **7.** $V = 7, R = 2$ **8.** $x = 5, y = 1$
9. $I = 7, V = -2$ **10.** $x = 2, y = 3$ **11.** $a = 1,$
$b = -3$ **12.** $I_1 = 3, I_2 = 4$ **13.** $x = 5, y = 1$
14. $I_1 = 4, I_2 = -1$ **15.** $a = 6, b = 10$ **16.** $I_2 = 4,$
$I_1 = 9$ **17.** $I_2 = 7, I_3 = -3$ **18.** $x = 1, y = 8$
19. $I_2 = 5, I_3 = 2$ **20.** $I_1 = 4, I_2 = 8$

JOB 8-12 Page 279 **1.** $x = 5, y = 3$ **2.** $x = 3,$
$y = 3$ **3.** $x = 5, y = 2$ **4.** $x = 2, y = 6$ **5.** $x = 2,$
$y = 7$ **6.** $x = 5, y = 1$ **7.** $x = 5, y = 3$ **8.** $x = 3,$
$y = 5$ **9.** $x = 1, y = 4$ **10.** $x = 4, y = 1$ **11.** $x = 1,$
$y = 4$ **12.** $x = 2, y = 4$

JOB 9-3 Page 294 **1.** (a) $I_T = 4$ A, (b) $V_2 = 20$ V,
$V_4 = 12$ V **2.** (a) $I_T = 7$ A, (b) $V_2 = 21$ V, $V_3 = 28$ V,
$V_5 = 14$ V **3.** (a) $I_T = 2.4$ A, (b) $V_2 = 14.4$ V,
$V_3 = 9.6$ V, $V_5 = 12$ V **4.** (a) $I_T = 3$ A, (b) $V_2 = 6$ V,
$V_3 = 12$ V, $V_5 = 18$ V **5.** (a) $I_T = 3$ A, (b) $V_2 = 12$ V,
$V_4 = 15$ V, $V_6 = 6$ V **6.** (a) $I_T = 0.4$ A, (b) $V_2 = 6$ V,
$V_4 = 10$ V, $V_6 = 18$ V **7.** 8.43 A **8.** $R = 5\,\Omega$

JOB 9-4 Page 299 **1.** $V_T = V_1 = V_2 = V_3 = 90$ V,
$I_T = 15$ A, $I_2 = 4.5$ A, $I_3 = 1.5$ A, $R_2 = 20\,\Omega$
2. $V_T = V_1 = V_2 = V_3 = 80$ V, $I_T = 10$ A, $I_3 = 4$ A,
$R_1 = 16\,\Omega, R_3 = 20\,\Omega$ **3.** $V_T = V_1 = V_2 = V_3 =$
300 V, $I_T = 20$ A, $I_2 = 2.5$ A, $I_3 = 7.5$ A, $R_2 = 120\,\Omega$
4. $V_T = 60$ V, $R_3 = 3\,\Omega$ **5.** $V_T = 108$ V, $R_3 = 6\,\Omega$
6. $V_T = 45$ V, $R_1 = 5\,\Omega$ **7.** $I_1 = 1.95$ A, $I_2 = 0.65$ A,
$V_T = 7.80$ V **8.** $I_1 = 2.475$ A, $I_2 = 5.5$ A, $V_T =$
247.5 V **9.** Same as Prob. 7 **10.** Check Problem 8
11. (a) $I_{16} = 6$ A, $I_{48} = 2$ A, $I_{24} = 4$ A, (b) $V_G = 96$ V
12. $I_1 = 1.875$ A, $I_2 = 5.625$ A, $V_T = 150$ V

JOB 9-5 Page 313 Set No. 1 **1.** $x = 2$ A, $y = 3$ A,
$z = 5$ A **2.** $x = 9$ A, $y = 4$ A, $z = 5$ A **3.** $x = 3$ A,
$y = 2$ A, $z = 1$ A **4.** $w = 7$ A, $x = 8$ A, $y = 1$ A,
$z = 5$ A **5.** $v = 12$ A, $w = 3$ A, $x = 5$ A, $y = 10$ A,
$z = 2$ A, $V_T = 104$ V **6.** $x = 2$ A, $y = 5$ A, $z = 3$ A
7. $x = 12$ A, $y = 4$ A, $z = 8$ A **8.** $x = 7$ A, $y = 2$ A,
$z = 5$ A

JOB 9-5 Page 315 (top) Set No. 2 **1.** $x = 4$ A,
$y = 2$ A, $z = 6$ A **2.** $x = 4$ A, $y = 1.6$ A, $z = 2.4$ A
3. $x = 1$ A, $y = 0.5$ A, $z = 0.5$ A **4.** $w = 3$ A, $x = 5$ A,

6

$y = 2$ A, $z = 12$ A **5.** $v = 6$ A, $w = 5$ A, $x = 3$ A, $y = 8$ A, $V_T = 170$ V, $z = 2$ A **6.** $x = 5$ A, $y = 7$ A, $z = 2$ A **7.** $x = 7$ A, $y = 3$ A, $z = 4$ A **8.** $x = 4$ A, $y = 3$ A, $z = 1$ A

JOB 9-5 Page 315 (bottom) Set No. 3 **1.** $x = 0.5$ A, $y = 1.5$ A, $z = 2$ A **2.** $x = 2$ A, $y = 5$ A, $z = 7$ A **3.** $x = 0.8$ A, $y = 0.6$ A, $z = 0.2$ A **4.** $w = 0.6$ A, $x = 0.8$ A, $y = 0.2$ A, $z = 2.2$ A **5.** $v = 1$ A, $w = 2.5$ A, $x = 0.5$ A, $y = 3$ A, $z = 2$ A, $V_T = 26$ V **6.** $x = 0.2$ A, $y = 0.9$ A, $z = 0.7$ A **7.** $x = 5.5$ A, $y = 2$ A, $z = 3.5$ A **8.** $x = 0.7$ A, $y = 0.3$ A, $z = 0.4$ A

JOB 9-7 Page 325 **1.** $R_a = R_b = R_c = 20$ Ω **2.** $R_a = 20$ Ω, $R_b = 5$ Ω, $R_c = 4$ Ω **3.** $R_a = 6$ Ω, $R_b = 4$ Ω, $R_c = 2.4$ Ω **4.** $R_a = 4.44$ Ω, $R_b = 6.67$ Ω, $R_c = 3.33$ Ω **5.** $R_{AD} = 3.67$ Ω **6.** $R_{AD} = 7.8$ Ω **7.** $R_{AD} = 10.95$ Ω **8.** $R_{AD} = 15.45$ Ω **9.** (a) $R_T = 5$ Ω, (b) $v = 5$ A, $w = 5$ A, $x = 4.5$ A, $y = 5.5$ A, $z = 0.5$ A, (c) $V_T = 50$ V **10.** (a) $R_T = 8.5$ Ω, (b) $v = 12$ A, $w = 4$ A, $x = 6$ A, $y = 10$ A, $z = 2$ A, (c) $V_T = 170$ V **11.** (a) $R_T = 12.67$ Ω, (b) $v = 4$ A, $w = 6$ A, $x = 7.87$ A, $y = 2.13$ A, $z = 1.87$ A, (c) $V_T = 126.7$ V **12.** (a) $R_T = 30$ Ω, (b) $I_T = 4$ A, (c) $I_5 = 2.67$ A, (d) $I_6 = 1.33$ A

JOB 9-8 Page 337 **1.** $I_L = 1$ A, $V_L = 10$ V **2.** $x = 9$ A, $y = 4$ A, $z = 5$ A, $V_3 = 48$ V **3.** $I_L = 12$ A, $V_L = 43.2$ V **4.** $y = 3$ A, $V_3 = 6$ V **5.** $I_L = 0.2$ A, $V_L = 4.6$ V **6.** $x = 4$ A, $y = 2$ A, $z = 6$ A **7.** $I_5 = 3$ A, $V_5 = 18$ V **8.** $w = 3$ A, $V_2 = 9$ V **9.** $I_L = 0.0025$ A, $V_L = 25$ V **10.** $I_L = 0.6$ A, $V_L = 24$ V

JOB 10-1 Page 348 **1.** 5.56 **2.** 1.01 Ω **3.** 3 **4.** 0.1 Ω **5.** 0.051 **6.** 0.25 Ω **7.** 0.747 **8.** (a) 2.78 Ω, (b) 1.32 Ω, (c) 0.64 Ω **9.** 0.21 **10.** (a) 0.152 Ω, (b) 0.03 Ω

JOB 10-2 Page 350 **1.** 15 mA **2.** 0.7 A **3.** 40.4 mA **4.** 30.6 A **5.** 70.7 A **6.** 102 mA

JOB 10-3 Page 353 **1.** (a) 290,000, (b) 168 V **2.** (a) 1999 Ω, (b) 12 V **3.** (a) 2995, (b) 21.6 V **4.** 24,000 Ω **5.** (a) 17,000, (b) 51,000 **6.** (a) 99,000 Ω, (b) 70 V **7.** (a) 45,000, (b) 95,000, (c) 145,000 **8.** 60,000 Ω

JOB 10-4 Page 355 **1.** 0.182 **2.** 45 mA **3.** 60.6 mA **4.** 100 Ω/V **5.** 333 Ω/V **6.** 135,000 Ω **7.** 50 μA **8.** 2500 Ω/V **9.** 1500 Ω **10.** (a) 100 Ω/V, (b) 12,000 Ω, (c) 60 V **11.** (a) 2250 Ω, (b) 12.8 V **12.** (a) 15 V, (b) 67 Ω/V, (c) 7000 Ω, 11,000 Ω **13.** 0.56 Ω **14.** 28.3 mA

JOB 10-5 Page 360 **1.** $R_1 = 50,000$ Ω, $R_2 = 7143$ Ω, $R_3 = 20,000$ Ω **2.** $R_1 = 10,000$ Ω, $R_2 = 1500$ Ω, $R_3 = 2000$ Ω, $R_4 = 909$ Ω **3.** $R_1 = 10,000$ Ω, R_2 3333 Ω, $R_3 = 1111$ Ω **4.** $R_1 = 10,000$ Ω, $R_2 = 5000$ Ω, $R_3 = 1429$ Ω **5.** $R_1 = 10,000$ Ω, $R_2 = 7143$ Ω, $R_3 = 12,500$ Ω **6.** $R_1 = 2143$ Ω, $R_2 = 2500$ Ω, $R_3 = 50$ Ω, $R_4 = 33$ Ω

JOB 10-6 Page 365 **1.** 1250 Ω **2.** 227 Ω **3.** 11.1 Ω **4.** 37.5 V **5.** $V_k = 33.3$ V, $V_x = 66.7$ V **6.** $V_k = 51.4$ V, $V_x = 68.6$ V **7.** (a) $V_1 = 25.6$ V, (b) $V_2 = 58.1$ V, (c) $V_3 = 116.3$ V **8.** $V_1 = 1.6$ V, $V_2 = 15.9$ V **9.** 130 V **10.** 3.75 V **11.** 0.1 V **12.** (a) 29 V, (b) 101.5 V

JOB 10-7 Page 367 **1.** 843 Ω **2.** 95.27 Ω **3.** 6.04 Ω **4.** 17.53 Ω **5.** 1289 Ω **6.** 1647 Ω **7.** 465 Ω **8.** 0.916 Ω **9.** 0.16 Ω **10.** 357.9 Ω

JOB 10-8 Page 371 **1.** $z = 9$ A **2.** $X = 10$ A **3.** $z = 3$ A **4.** $I_3 = 0.018$ A **5.** $I_5 = 2.25$ A

JOB 10-9 Page 378 **1.** (a) $I_{RL} = 1.44$ mA, (b) $V_{RL} = 7.2$ V, (c) $V_C = -2.8$ V **2.** (a) $I_L = 1.72$ mA, (b) $V_{RL} = 3.44$ V, (c) $V_C = -6.56$ V **3.** (a) $I_C = 0.25$ mA, (b) $I_E = 0.25$ mA, (c) $V_{RL} = 10$ V, (d) $V_C = -3$ V, (e) $V_{RE} = 0.5$ V, (f) $V_{CE} = 2.5$ V **4.** (a) $I_C = 0.4$ mA, (b) $I_E = 0.4$ mA, (c) $V_{RL} = 8$ V, (d) $V_C = -6$ V, (e) $V_{RE} = 2$ V, (f) $V_{CE} = 4$ V

JOB 10-10 Page 381 **1.** (a) $I_C = 1$ mA, (b) $V_{RL} = 1$ V, (c) $V_C = -9$ V **2.** (a) $I_C = 2$ mA, (b) $V_{RL} = 4$ V, (c) $V_C = -4$ V **3.** (a) $I_E = 3.67$ mA, (b) $V_E = -0.73$ V, (c) $I_C = 3.63$ mA, (d) $V_{RL} = 3.63$ V, (e) $V_C = -4.37$ V **4.** (a) $I_E = 2$ mA, (b) $V_E = -0.28$ V, (c) $I_C = 1.95$ mA, (d) $V_{RL} = 3.90$ V, (e) $V_C = -6.1$ V

JOB 10-11 Page 386 **1.** 4×10^{-6} A **2.** $\beta = 100$ **3.** $V_{BE} = 11.5$ mV **4.** $V_{RC} = 2.5$ V

JOB 10-12 Page 391 **1.** $R_1 = 12$ Ω, $R_2 = 3.75$ Ω **2.** $R_1 = 30$ Ω, $R_2 = 60$ Ω **3.** $R_1 = 5$ Ω, $R_2 = 10$ Ω **4.** $R_1 = 50$ Ω, $R_2 = 100$ Ω **5.** $R_1 = 36$ Ω, $R_2 = 40$ Ω **6.** $R_1 = 18$ Ω, $R_2 = 2.22$ Ω **7.** $R_1 = 20$ Ω, $R_2 = 400$ Ω **8.** $R_1 = 7.5$ Ω, $R_2 = 3.33$ Ω **9.** $R_1 = 75$ Ω, $R_2 = 33.3$ Ω **10.** $R_1 = 6.67$ Ω, $R_2 = 40$ Ω

JOB 10-12 Page 393 **1.** $R_1 = R_3 = 20$ Ω, $R_2 = 80$ Ω **2.** $R_1 = R_3 = 40$ Ω, $R_2 = 480$ Ω **3.** $R_1 = R_3 = 20$ Ω, $R_2 = 80$ Ω **4.** $R_1 = R_3 = 100$ Ω, $R_2 = 750$ Ω **5.** $R_1 = R_3 = 7.14$ Ω, $R_2 = 3.43$ Ω **6.** $R_1 = R_3 = 267$ Ω, $R_2 = 166.8$ Ω **7.** $R_1 = R_2 = 77.7$ Ω, $R_2 = 25.3$ Ω

JOB 10-13 Page 395   **1.** $R_1 = 20\ \Omega$—10 W, $R_2 = 40\ \Omega$—5 W, $R_L = 40\ \Omega$—5 W   **2.** $R_s = 10$ W, $R_1 = 7$ W, $R_2 = 2$ W   **3.** $R_1 = 10\ \Omega$—55 W, $R_2 = 25\ \Omega$—113 W, $R_3 = 20\ \Omega$—113 W   **4.** $R_1 = \frac{1}{8}$ W, $R_2 = \frac{1}{8}$ W   **5.** $R_1 = 3\ \Omega$, 7 W, $R_2 = 4\ \Omega$, 7 W, $R_3 = 12\ \Omega$, 2 W   **6.** $R_1 = 10$ W, $R_2 = 15$ W, $R_3 = 10$ W

JOB 11-1 Page 398   **1.** 100 Ω **2.** 0.765 lb   **3.** 17.25 A   **4.** No   **5.** 70.5 V   **6.** 90%   **7.** 93.3%   **8.** 57.6 W   **9.** 117.6 V   **10.** $81.25   **11.** $79.63   **12.** 20%   **13.** $3.33   **14.** 12.8 oz

JOB 11-2 Page 399   **1.** 0.38   **2.** 0.6   **3.** 0.06   **4.** 0.19   **5.** 0.04   **6.** 0.264   **7.** 0.036   **8.** 1   **9.** 1.25   **10.** 0.005   **11.** 0.167   **12.** 0.0075   **13.** 0.625   **14.** 0.01   **15.** 0.125   **16.** 0.009   **17.** 0.0225   **18.** 0.055   **19.** 0.0425   **20.** 0.005

JOB 11-2 Page 400   **1.** 50%   **2.** 4%   **3.** 20%   **4.** 7.5%   **5.** 145%   **6.** 0.8%   **7.** 100%   **8.** 87%   **9.** 62½%   **10.** 9.2%   **11.** 22.2%   **12.** 15%   **13.** 70%   **14.** 300%   **15.** 5½%

JOB 11-2 Page 401   **1.** 25%   **2.** 37½%   **3.** 40%   **4.** 80%   **5.** 62½%   **6.** 18.75%   **7.** 30%   **8.** 60%   **9.** 50%   **10.** 90%   **11.** 65%   **12.** 9.38%   **13.** 66⅔%   **14.** 83⅓%   **15.** 45.5%   **16.** 42.9%   **17.** 33⅓%   **18.** 40%   **19.** 22.2%   **20.** 86⅔%

JOB 11-2 Page 403   **1.** 33   **2.** $30   **3.** $7.50   **4.** $0.23   **5.** $56.25   **6.** 300 ft   **7.** 17.25 A   **8.** 50   **9.** 116.7 V   **10.** 31.5 lines   **11.** 5   **12.** 4.4 V, 215.6 V   **13.** 7.5 W   **14.** $18.13   **15.** $19.18   **16.** 0.35 A

JOB 11-2 Page 404   **1.** 25%   **2.** 37½%   **3.** 40%   **4.** 14.1%   **5.** 2%   **6.** 133⅓%   **7.** 150%   **8.** 35%   **9.** 33⅓%   **10.** 18.9%   **11.** 12½%   **12.** 3.33%   **13.** 40%   **14.** 38.5%   **15.** 2.25%   **16.** 83⅓%   **17.** 20%   **18.** 12%   **19.** 5%   **20.** 20%

JOB 11-2 Page 406   **1.** 20   **2.** 500   **3.** 40   **4.** 1000   **5.** 2000   **6.** 150 V   **7.** $238.33   **8.** 5.88 hp   **9.** 15 A   **10.** 119.4 V

JOB 11-2 Page 407   **1.** (a) 0.62, (b) 0.03, (c) 0.056, (d) 0.008, (e) 1.16, (f) 0.045, (g) 0.0625   **2.** (a) 40%, (b) 8%, (c) 60%, (d) 200%, (e) 62½%, (f) 4½%, (g) 500%   **3.** (a) 75%, (b) 60%, (c) 42.9%, (d) 30%, (e) 23.1%, (f) 16⅔%, (g) 46.1%   **4.** 17.28   **5.** $90   **6.** 16⅔%   **7.** 40%   **8.** 20   **9.** $48.75   **10.** 400   **11.** 20.8%   **12.** 0.45   **13.** 1.5%   **14.** 48   **15.** 116.4 V   **16.** $97.50, $357.50, $22.17   **17.** $22.80, $307.80   **18.** 0.9 W = 1 W   **19.** $88.80

JOB 11-3 Page 409   **1.** 6500 W   **2.** 1500 W   **3.** 2.3 kW   **4.** 3.5 hp   **5.** 50 W   **6.** 1⅓ hp

7. ¾ kW   **8.** 2⅓ hp   **9.** 1.69 kW   **10.** 10 hp   **11.** 0.094 kW   **12.** 562.5 W   **13.** 5.33 hp   **14.** 3⅜ kW   **15.** 13⅓ hp   **16.** 11⅔ hp

JOB 11-4 Page 411   **1.** 83⅓%   **2.** 93.75%   **3.** 96%   **4.** 83⅓%   **5.** 88.9%   **6.** 83⅓%   **7.** 91.3%   **8.** 3750 W, 71%   **9.** 80.2%, 19.8%   **10.** 93.2%

JOB 11-5 Page 414   **1.** 3.6 hp   **2.** 62.5 W   **3.** 0.587 hp   **4.** 0.74 hp   **5.** 4508 W   **6.** 70.4 W   **7.** 2647 W   **8.** 7.4 hp   **9.** 2200 W, 3.26 hp   **10.** 15.7 A   **11.** 220 V   **12.** 6.21 kW

JOB 11-6 Page 416

1.

R_L	I_L	P_{RL}	P_{Pth}	Eff, %
6	¾ A	5.63	3.38	38
8	⅔ A	4.44	3.56	45
10	⅗ A	3.60	3.60	50
12	6⁄11 A	2.98	3.57	55
14	½ A	2.58	3.50	58

2. 10.125 V   **3.** $R = 100\ \Omega$

JOB 11-7 Page 417   **1.** (a) 0.5 kW, (b) ⅔ hp, (c) 1500 W, (d) 1125 W, (e) 13.3 hp, (f) 7.5 kW   **2.** 86.5%   **3.** 91.4%   **4.** 93%   **5.** 0.62 hp   **6.** 8.28 kW   **7.** 0.625 kW   **8.** 21.6 A

JOB 12-1 Page 420   **1.** 2:5   **2.** 4:1   **3.** 9:1   **4.** 10:11   **5.** 3:4   **6.** 0.007 Ω **7.** $23.75   **8.** 45 oz   **9.** 15 V   **10.** 104 Ω **11.** $\frac{R_1}{R_2} = \frac{I_2}{I_1}$ **12.** 2 V

JOB 12-2 Page 424   **1.** 1:4   **2.** 3:1   **3.** 2:3   **4.** 21:4   **5.** 2:1   **6.** 4:1   **7.** 4:1   **8.** 1:2   **9.** (a) 3:2, (b) 2:3   **10.** 7:6   **11.** 1:4   **12.** 4:1   **13.** 1:4   **14.** 25:4   **15.** 83.3%   **16.** 100   **17.** 171   **18.** 1:35   **19.** 40   **20.** 87.4%   **21.** 10   **22.** 5   **23.** 1:48   **24.** (a) 2:3, (b) 3:2   **25.** (a) 2 V, (b) 1.7%, (c) 98.3%

JOB 12-2 Page 427   **1.** 2750 lb   **2.** $0.98   **3.** 4½ h   **4.** 27 ft   **5.** 71.4 ft³   **6.** 150 lb   **7.** 1000 Ω **8.** 51 Ω **9.** 45 V   **10.** 5.64 V

JOB 12-2 Page 431   **1.** 5 in   **2.** 144 rpm   **3.** 66.7   **4.** 1000   **5.** 500   **6.** $R_1 = 320\ \Omega$ **7.** 0.08 A   **8.** $R_2 = 40\ \Omega$ **9.** 0.93 Ω **10.** $V_s = 300$ V   **11.** 0.25 A   **12.** $I_s = 80$ A

JOB 12-3 Page 432   **1.** (a) 1:3, (b) 1:6, (c) 1:10, (d) 5:8, (e) 3:4   **2.** $R_1 = 150\ \Omega$ **3.** 36   **4.** 49   **5.** 72   **6.** 32   **7.** 0.6 A   **8.** $I_2 = 5.4$ A   **9.** 10 V   **10.** $I_p = 1$ A

JOB 12-4   Page 434   **1.** No. 21, 0.0285 in
2. 101.9 mil, 0.1019 in   **3.** No. 2, 250 mil
4. No. 16, 50.82 mil   **5.** No. 6, 162 mil
6. No. 4, 0.2043 in   **7.** 64.08 mil, 0.0641 in
8. 80.81 mil, 0.0808 in   **9.** No. 18, 0.0403 in
10. No. 14, 62.5 mil

JOB 12-4   Page 436   **1.** 0.010 in, 100 mil
2. 50 mil, 2500 cmil   **3.** 0.064 in, 64 mil
4. 0.06 in, 3600 cmil   **5.** 32 mil, 1024 cmil
6. 0.0975 in, 97.5 mil   **7.** 0.0872 in, 7604 cmil
8. 250 mil; 62,500 cmil   **9.** 0.173 in, 173 mil
10. 102 mil; 10,404 cmil   **11.** 397,886 cmil   **12.** 598 mil

JOB 12-5   Page 438   **1.** 19.6 Ω   **2.** 706 Ω
3. 12.5 Ω   **4.** 63.7 Ω

JOB 12-6   Page 440   **1.** 3.68 Ω   **2.** 3.21 Ω
3. 4.06 Ω   **4.** 6.09 Ω   **5.** 1.205 Ω, 5 A   **6.** 9.39 A
7. 32.82 Ω, 3.35 A   **8.** 0.1256 Ω   **9.** 33.7 Ω, 6.74 V
10. 0.161 Ω, 9.3 Ω, 11.8 A

JOB 12-7   Page 442   **1.** 52.5 Ω   **2.** 9.375 Ω
3. 508 V   **4.** 6.09 Ω   **5.** 12.86 Ω

JOB 12-8   Page 444   **1.** 0.104 Ω   **2.** 24.7 Ω
3. 0.0062 Ω   **4.** 5.19 Ω, 1.16 A   **5.** 4.46 Ω,
24.6 A, 2.71 kW   **6.** 30.3 Ω   **7.** (*a*) 0.145 A,
(*b*) 0.87 W   **8.** 1.3 Ω   **9.** 0.2 V   **10.** 0.324 Ω

JOB 12-9   Page 446   **1.** 1.7 Ω   **2.** 4.61 Ω   **3.** 96.1 ft
4. 12 ft, 6.11 A, 672 W   **5.** 3 ft   **6.** 0.121 ft   **7.** 370 ft
8. 2.3 Ω, 39.2 ft   **9.** Nichrome   **10.** 316 ft

JOB 12-10   Page 448   **1.** 9.4 mil   **2.** 106 mil
3. 6.93 mil   **4.** No. 16   **5.** 32 mil   **6.** No. 30
7. No. 17   **8.** No. 0000   **9.** No. 12   **10.** No. 13

JOB 12-11   Page 457   **1.** 1.93 Ω/kft   **2.** 2.05 Ω/kft
3. 3.25 Ω/kft   **4.** 0.2015 Ω   **5.** No. 8   **6.** No. 12
7. No. 10   **8.** 55   **9.** 45   **10.** 10

JOB 12-12   Page 458   **1.** (*a*) 25 mil, No. 22,
(*b*) 102 mil, No. 10, (*c*) 125 mil, No. 8, (*d*) 128 mil,
No. 8   **2.** (*a*) 225 cmil, (*b*) 1600 cmil, (*c*) 100 cmil,
(*d*) 41,616 cmil   **3.** 44.9 Ω   **4.** 10.2 Ω, 1.53 V
5. 1.4 Ω   **6.** 0.29 Ω   **7.** 3.07 ft   **8.** 3 mil

JOB 13-1   Page 463   **1.** 55 A   **2.** No. 8   **3.** No. 6
4. No. 8   **5.** 34.5 V   **6.** No. 6   **7.** 0.000 25 Ω/ft
8. No. 10   **9.** No. 3   **10.** 204.3 mil, 0.2043 in

JOB 13-2   Page 465   **1.** No. 6   **2.** No. 8   **3.** No. 4
4. No. 2   **5.** No. 1   **6.** No. 14   **7.** No. 10
8. No. 12   **9.** RH = No. 0, V = No. 1, AF = No. 3
10. No. 8

JOB 13-3   Page 470   **1.** No. 4   **2.** No. 12   **3.** No. 0
4. No. 6   **5.** No. 3   **6.** No. 00   **7.** No. 12   **8.** No. 4
9. (*a*) 5250 W, (*b*) 250 W, (*c*) 44 A, (*d*) 5.7 V,
(*e*) No. 1   **10.** No. 2   **11.** 450 ft   **12.** (*a*) 0.2 Ω,
(*b*) 118 V, (*c*) 120 ft

JOB 13-4   Page 472 (top)   **1.** 95   **2.** 90   **3.** 30
4. 115   **5.** 30   **6.** 130   **7.** 135   **8.** 175   **9.** 25
10. 60

JOB 13-4   Page 472 (bottom)   **1.** 47.85
2. 63.8   **3.** 110.7   **4.** 70.5   **5.** 94   **6.** 77.35
7. 22.75   **8.** 17.75   **9.** 11.6   **10.** 43.55

JOB 13-5   Page 472   **1.** 40 A   **2.** No. 8   **3.** No. 3
4. 80.8 mil   **5.** No. 14   **6.** No. 10   **7.** No. 10
8. No. 2   **9.** No. 1   **10.** No. 000   **11.** No. 14
12. 427 ft

JOB 14-1   Page 483   **1.** sin = 0.2462, cos = 0.9692,
tan = 0.2540   **2.** sin = 0.2800, cos = 0.9600, tan =
0.2917   **3.** sin = 0.3243, cos = 0.9459, tan = 0.3428
4. sin = 0.9756, cos = 0.2195, tan = 4.4444   **5.** sin
= 0.8823, cos = 0.4706, tan = 1.8750

JOB 14-2   Page 485 (top)   **1.** 18°   **2.** 40°   **3.** 80°
4. 9°   **5.** 30°   **6.** 47°   **7.** 30°   **8.** 45°   **9.** 60°
10. 20°

JOB 14-2   Page 485 (bottom)   **1.** 15°   **2.** 41°
3. 58°   **4.** 14°   **5.** 65°   **6.** 62°   **7.** 16°   **8.** 81°
9. 46°   **10.** 75°

JOB 14-3   Page 488

	∠A	∠B		∠A	∠B
1.	53°	37°	**7.**	51°	39°
2.	35°	55°	**8.**	31°	59°
3.	30°	60°	**9.**	11°	79°
4.	58°	32°	**10.**	58°	32°
5.	55°	35°	**11.**	67°	113°
6.	17°	73°	**12.**	63°	117°

13. 3°   **14.** 6°   **15.** 58°

JOB 14-4   Page 493   **1.** 10 in, 30°   **2.** 16.71 ft, 50°
3. 89.4 ft, 40°   **4.** 353.2 W, 62°   **5.** 151 Ω, 60°
6. 33.1 Ω, 65°   **7.** 940.4 ft, 62°   **8.** 21.1 in, 55°
9. 123 Ω, 75°   **10.** 24.02 V, 75°   **11.** 35.1 m, 33 m
12. 4.68 in   **13.** 8.5 cm   **14.** 4.24 cm   **15.** 9.1 m
16. I_x = 6 A, I_y = 8 A   **17.** I_x = 12.69 A, I_y = 5.92 A
18. X_C = 728 Ω   **19.** 2128 Ω   **20.** *a* = 0.650 in,
b = 1.025 in, *c* = 0.860 in, *d* = 0.515 in, *e* = 0.892 in

JOB 14-5   Page 495   **1.** 0.5878   **2.** 0.2079
3. 2.6051   **4.** 0.7880   **5.** 0.9063   **6.** 36°   **7.** 65°
8. 80°   **9.** 11°   **10.** 46°   **11.** 17°   **12.** 8°   **13.** 73°

14. 46° 15. 37° 16. 30° 17. 71° 18. 14°
19. 58° 20. 77° 21. 930 W 22. 594 W 23. 38.5
24. 11.2 Ω 25. 833 Ω 26. 30.5 ft 27. 2828 W
28. 1768 W 29. 236 V 30. 10.5 Ω 31. 81°, 99°
32. 66° 33. 3° 34. 8.83 m 35. 1.72 in 36. 80 in
37. 23° 38. 76 cm 39. 233.3 Ω 40. I_x = 13 A, I_y = 7.5 A

JOB 15-1 Page 504 1. (*a*) 0.54 A, (*b*) 0.63 A, (*c*) 0.66 A, (*d*) 0.762 A, (*e*) 0.79 A, (*f*) 0.87 A, (*g*) 0.99 A 2. (*a*) 0.09 Ω, (*b*) 0.24 Ω, (*c*) 0.4 Ω, (*d*) 0.63 Ω, (*e*) 0.96 Ω, (*f*) 1.44 Ω, (*g*) 0.46 Ω, (*h*) 0.21 Ω, (*i*) 0.16 Ω, (*j*) 0.11 Ω 3. and 4. See student's work. 5. Max eff = 80%; 50 hp

JOB 15-3 Page 516 1. 10,000 m 2. 500 kHz 3. 126.4 V 4. 87 V 5. 17° 6. 25.9 A 7. 43.3 A 8. 10° 9. (*a*) 30°, (*b*) 37°, (*c*) 60° 10. (*a*) 0 V, (*b*) 25.88 V, (*c*) 50 V, (*d*) 70.71 V, (*e*) 86.6 V, (*f*) 96.59 V, (*g*) 100 V, (*h*) 61.25 V

JOB 15-4 Page 519

	Max	Eff	Instant	Phase Angle
1.	—	24.7	17.5	—
2.	—	322	293	—
3.	622	—	476	—
4.	35.35	—	30.6	—
5.	—	109.6	77.5	—
6.	—	7.07	7.07	—
7.	155.5	—	140.9	—
8.	28.3	—	27.3	—
9.	35	24.7	—	—
10.	464	328	—	—
11.	—	70.7		26°
12.	—	14.14	—	16°

13. 17.3 V 14. 156 V 15. (*a*) 10.6 A, (*b*) 900 W 16. 3111 V 17. 285 W

JOB 15-5 Page 522 1. 90 V 2. 500 Hz 3. (*a*) 150 mV, (*b*) 0.2 Hz 4. 90 V, 100 Hz 5. 600 V 6. 37.5 ms 7. 2.5 ms 8. ⅓ V 9. ⅓ V 10. 10 s

JOB 15-6 Page 525 1. 60 Ω 2. 2.4 A 3. 110 V 4. 150 Ω, 96 W 5. 160 V, 3.2 W 6. 0.4 A, 44 W 7. 1.82 A, 60.4 Ω 8. 600 W 9. 111 V, 24.7 Ω 10. 1.44 Ω

JOB 15-7 Page 528 1. 10 2. 25 3. 16 4. 56 5. 26.5 6. 18.5 7. 4.5 8. 42 9. 72.11 m

10. 8 ft 11. 7.62 ft 12. 7.5 ft 13. 46 ft 14. 4.6 in 15. 32 in

JOB 15-8 Page 531 1. 1 A 2. 0.025 A, 0 W 3. 25.12 V 4. 62.8 V, 0 W 5. 3000 Ω, 7.96 H

JOB 15-9 Page 538 1. Student answers will vary 2. 420 Hz 3. Student answers will vary 4. T 5. F 6. T 7. T 8. F 9. T 10. F

JOB 16-3 Page 547 1. (*a*) 439.6 Ω, (*b*) 8792 Ω 2. (*a*) 12, 560 Ω, (*b*) 3.2 mA 3. (*a*) 7536 Ω, (*b*) 0.02 A 4. (*a*) 41,500 Ω, (*b*) 1 mA 5. 37.7 Ω 6. 1000 kHz 7. 5 H 8. 942 Ω 9. 62,800 Ω 10. (*a*) 188 Ω, (*b*) 37,680 Ω 11. 2864 Ω 12. 94,200 Ω 13. 2.7 mH 14. 4 μH 15. 255 μH

JOB 16-4 Page 555 1. (*a*) 13 Ω, (*b*) 8 A, (*c*) V_R = 40 V, V_L = 96 V, (*d*) 67°, (*e*) 39.1%, (*f*) 321 W 2. (*a*) 112 Ω, (*b*) 1 A, (*c*) V_R = 50 V, V_L = 100 V, (*d*) 63°, (*e*) 44.6%, (*f*) 50 W 3. 0.92 A, 74° 4. 36 Ω 5. (*a*) 150 Ω, (*b*) 170 Ω, (*c*) 85 V 6. 200 Hz, 1 mA 7. 1.5 μA 8. (*a*) 10 A, (*b*) 2 kW 9. 4.5 A 10. (*a*) 1005 Ω, (*b*) 1122 Ω, (*c*) 5.61 V 11. 3770 Ω, 0.01 A 12. 2.43 H 13. 28.6 H 14. 3.75 mA, 0.07 W 15. X_L = 7.5 Ω; 43°

Job 16-5 Page 558 1. 4 2. 6 3. 31.4 4. 37 Ω 5. (*a*) 10, (*b*) 1000 Ω 6. 96.3 Ω 7. (*a*) 9420 Ω, (*b*) 10,665 Ω, (*c*) 3.8 A 8. (*a*) 3768 Ω, (*b*) 9.4, (*c*) 3768 Ω, (*d*) 0.032 A 9. (*a*) 314 Ω, (*b*) 330 Ω 10. (*a*) 3000 Ω, (*b*) 3000 Ω, (*c*) 31,400 Ω, (*d*) 94,200 Ω 11. 0.7 mA 12. (*a*) 3000 Ω, (*b*) 3065 Ω, (*c*) 4343 Ω

JOB 16-6 Page 561 1. 3.18 H 2. 14.6 H 3. 0.796 H 4. 73 mH 5. 0.51 H 6. 0.45 H

JOB 16-7 Page 562 1. (*a*) 125.6 Ω, (*b*) 1256 Ω, (*c*) 12,560 Ω, (*d*) 125,600 Ω 2. (*a*) 6280 Ω, (*b*) 0.8 mA 3. 3140 Ω 4. 1.59 H 5. 60 6. 89 Ω 7. 30 Ω 8. (*a*) 157 Ω, (*b*) 157 Ω, (*c*) 19 mA 9. 0.61 H 10. 0.239 H 11. 0.25 H 12. 1.5 H

JOB 16-8 Page 566 1. 0.365 mH 2. X = 0.58 Ω 3. (*a*) 32.30 mH, (*b*) 117 V

JOB 16-9 Page 570 1. 360 V 2. (*a*) 11 : 1, (*b*) 11 : 1 3. (*a*) 48 : 1, (*b*) 48 : 1 4. 45 V 5. 600 turns 6. 1250 turns 7. 6000 V 8. 80,000 turns 9. 1.5 V 10. 50 turns 11. 300 turns 12. (*a*) 22 : 1, (*b*) 110 V, (*c*) 2200 turns 13. 240 V 14. (*a*) 27 turns, (*b*) 75 turns 15. (*a*) 2 turns, (*b*) 5¼ turns, (*c*) 500 turns 16. (*a*) 3.5 : 1, (*b*) 142.8 A

JOB 16-10 Page 574 **1.** 2 A **2.** 0.2 A **3.** (*a*) 0.16 A, (*b*) 19.2 W **4.** (*a*) 2 A, (*b*) 15 V, (*c*) 30 W **5.** (*a*) 0.136 A, (*b*) 7.5 V **6.** 20.9 A **7.** (*a*) 0.086 A, (*b*) 9.45 W **8.** (*a*) 42.5 A, (*b*) 46 V, (*c*) 1955 W **9.** (*a*) 5 A, (*b*) 1500 V **10.** 8.1 A **11.** 511 A **12.** (*a*) 135 V, (*b*) 18 A, (*c*) 0.09 A, (*d*) 2430 W

JOB 16-11 Page 576 **1.** 20:1 **2.** 1:3 **3.** 4:1 **4.** 30:1 **5.** 1:5 **6.** 1:50 **7.** 12,100 Ω **8.** 41.8:1 or 42:1 (approx.) **9.** 8:1 **10.** 31.6:1 or 32:1 (approx.) **11.** 39:1 **12.** 2.9:1 or 3:1 (approx.) **13.** 1:3 **14.** 28,800 Ω

JOB 16-12 Page 578 **1.** (*a*) 176 turns, (*b*) 8:1 **2.** 6000 V **3.** 1750 turns **4.** 160 V **5.** (*a*) 100 turns, (*b*) 22.7 turns **6.** 0.454 A **7.** (*a*) 1.25 A, (*b*) 150 W **8.** (*a*) 2.5 A, (*b*) 24 V, (*c*) 60 W **9.** (*a*) 14 A, (*b*) 28.75 V, (*c*) 402.5 W **10.** 93% **11.** (*a*) 135 W, (*b*) 2.7 A **12.** 12.5:1 **13.** 45,000 Ω **14.** (*a*) 240 V, (*b*) 12 A, (*c*) 40 mA, (*d*) 2880 W

JOB 16-13 Page 586 **1.** 1210 Ω **2.** 0.74 A **3.** 0.392 H **4.** (*a*) 2233 Ω, (*b*) 0.15 H, (*c*) 12 **5.** 0.209 Ω **6.** 0.71 Ω

JOB 16-14 Page 590 **1.** 87.5 percent **2.** 80% **3.** (*a*) 180 W, (*b*) 168 W, (*c*) 93.3% **4.** (*a*) 87.5%, (*b*) 0.8 A **5.** 80% **6.** (*a*) 920 W, (*b*) 18.4 A **7.** (*a*) 10,417 W, (*b*) 5.21 A **8.** (*a*) 100 W, (*b*) 125 V **9.** (*a*) 77 W, (*b*) 88 V **10.** 91.9% **11.** (*a*) $R_m = $ 8.52 Ω, (*b*) $R_1 = 0.02$ Ω

JOB 16-15 Page 602
1.

Cable Size	Resistance, R	cmil, A	K
4	0.0318	41,470	13.18746
2	0.0203	66,360	13.47108
1	0.0162	83,690	13.55778
0	0.0130	105,500	13.715

2.

Cable Size	Resistance, R	Reactance, X	Impedance, Z	Drop, V	%
4	0.053	0.00490	0.0532260275	12.77	11.1
2	0.0335	0.00457	0.033810278	8.11	7.1
1	0.0267	0.00440	0.0270601183	6.49	5.6
0	0.0212	0.00410	0.0215928229	5.18	4.5
00	0.017	0.00396	0.0174551311	4.19	3.6
000	0.0138	0.00386	0.0143296755	3.44	3
0000	0.01103	0.00381	0.01097	2.63	2.3

JOB 17-2 Page 609 **1.** 373 pF **2.** All 75-V capacitors **3.** 5065 pF **4.** 5.0003 μF **5.** 30,085 pF **6.** 0.023 μF **7.** 150 pF **8.** 1.94 μF

JOB 17-3 Page 612 **1.** 1.333 μF **2.** 20 μF, 350 V **3.** 19 pF **4.** (*a*) 909 pF, (*b*) 522 pF **5.** 31 to 162 pF **6.** 0.003 75 μF, 1600 V **7.** 3 μF **8.** 0.010 91 μF **9.** 8 μF **10.** 22.5 pF

JOB 17-4 Page 616 **1.** (*a*) 17,667 Ω, (*b*) 5300 Ω, (*c*) 662 Ω **2.** 872 Ω **3.** 0.19 A **4.** 7.95 Ω, 0.3 A **5.** 400 pF; 3975 Ω **6.** 16 A **7.** 1.67 μF **8.** 0.15 A **9.** (*a*) 15.9 Ω, (*b*) 3.18 Ω, (*c*) 0.795 Ω **10.** 21.2 Ω, 0.5 A **11.** 13,250 Ω **12.** 79.5 Ω **13.** 60 Hz **14.** 0.5 A **15.** (*a*) 31.8 Ω, (*b*) 0.636 Ω **16.** 0.75 Ω **17.** 0.02 μF **18.** 60.2 μF **19.** 442 μF

JOB 17-5 Page 620 **1.** (*a*) 2.25 A, (*b*) 0, (*c*) 0 W **2.** 0.1 A **3.** 124 Ω **4.** 1325 Ω, 4.5 mA **5.** 39.75 Ω, 0.1 A **6.** (*a*) 8 V, (*b*) 0 W **7.** 0.25 mA **8.** 265 V **9.** 100 Ω, 0.001 59 μF **10.** 92.75 V

JOB 17-6 Page 621 **1.** 265 μF **2.** 12 μF **3.** 2.94 μF **4.** 1.27 μF **5.** 10 μF

JOB 17-7 Page 626 **1.** (*a*) 17 A, (*b*) 7.06 Ω, (*c*) 28°, (*d*) 88.2%, (*e*) 1799 W **2.** (*a*) 4.47 A, (*b*) 23.7 Ω, (*c*) 27°, (*d*) 89.5%, (*e*) 424 W **3.** (*a*) 2.23 A, (*b*) 53.9 Ω, (*c*) 63°, (*d*) 44.8%, (*e*) 120 W **4.** (*a*) 0.1 A, (*b*) 80 Ω **5.** 0.566 A **6.** 100%, 2%, yes **7.** 44.8% AF, 0.05% RF; Yes, but not a good one. **8.** (*a*) 4.72 μA, (*b*) 127,000 Ω **9.** 200 μA

JOB 17-8 Page 629 **1.** 0.0497 μF **2.** 0.0008 μF **3.** 1.6 μF **4.** 12.5 μF, 360 V **5.** 187 pF **6.** 146 pF **7.** (*a*) 26.5 Ω, (*b*) 0.053 Ω **8.** 393 Ω **9.** 44.7 Ω **10.** 4450 Ω **11.** 0.381 μF **12.** 0.096 μF

JOB 18-2 Page 635 **1.** (*a*) 17 Ω, (*b*) 7 A, (*c*) $V_R = 56$ V, $V_C = 105$ V, (*d*) 62°, (*e*) 47.1%, (*f*) 392 W **2.** (*a*) 67 Ω, (*b*) 2 A, (*c*) $V_R = 60$ V, $V_C = 120$ V, (*d*) 63°, (*e*) 44.8%, (*f*) 120 W **3.** (*a*) 141 Ω, (*b*) 0.8 A, (*c*) $V_R = 80$ V, $V_C = 80$ V, (*d*) 45°, (*e*) 70.9%, (*f*) 64 W **4.** 0.33 A, 88° **5.** (*a*) 159,000 Ω,

(b) 18,800 Ω **6.** 1 V **7.** (a) 500 Ω, (b) 400 Ω,
(c) 6.63 μF **8.** (a) 0.005 A, (b) 0.005 A, (c) 20,000 Ω,
(d) 0.1325 μF **9.** 113 Hz **10.** 19.5 Ω

JOB 18-3 Page 644 **1.** (a) 65 Ω, (b) 2 A,
(c) V_R = 32 V, V_L = 166 V, V_C = 40 V, (d) 76°,
(e) 24.6%, (f) 64 W **2.** (a) 85 Ω, (b) 1.5 A, (c) 65°,
(d) 42.4%, (e) 81 W **3.** (a) X_L = 6280 Ω,
X_C = 3180 Ω, (b) 5060 Ω, (c) 0.025 A, (d) 37°,
(e) 79.1%, (f) 2.47 W **4.** 182 Ω, 0.55 μA **5.** 0.7 V
6. 40.1 Ω **7.** 1.5 A **8.** (a) 340 Ω, (b) 300 Ω,
(c) 434 Ω **9.** 271 Ω **10.** 1 kHz, 50 Ω, 0.2 A
11. 0.01 H **12.** (a) 2 A, (b) 55 Ω, (c) 30 Ω, (d) 57.5 μF

JOB 18-4 Page 648 **1.** (a) 795 kHz, (b) 50 Ω
2. 1590 kHz **3.** (a) 2 kHz, (b) 502 Ω, (c) 502 Ω,
(d) 12 Ω, (e) 0.5 A, (f) 251 V **4.** 176.7 kHz
5. 1988 kHz **6.** 1988 kHz **7.** 1988 kHz **8.** 460
kHz. The primary is a parallel circuit because the
source of voltage is outside the combination. The
electron may follow more than one path through
either L or C, forming a parallel circuit. The secondary is a series circuit because the source of voltage
is the emf generated in the coil itself. The electrons
must follow the single path through the C and L, pro-
ducing a series circuit. **9.** 1590 kHz **10.** 480 kHz

JOB 18-5 Page 651 **1.** 84.3 μH **2.** 127 pF
3. 0.506 H **4.** 23.4 pF **5.** 35.1 μF **6.** 176 pF
7. 72 μH **8.** 225 pF **9.** 2.53 mH **10.** 47 and 422 pF

JOB 18-6 Page 654 **1.** 180 V **2.** 0.1 A, 0 W
3. 5.3 H **4.** 159 V **5.** (a) 6360 Ω, (b) 7.9 mA,
(c) V_R = 7.9 V, V_L = 49.6 V, (d) 81°, (e) 15.7%,
(f) 0.06 W **6.** (a) 223 Ω, (b) 0.538 A,
(c) V_R = 107.6 V, V_C = 53.8 V, (d) 26°, (e) 89.7%,
(f) 57.9 W **7.** (a) 41.2 Ω, (b) 4790 Ω **8.** (a) 1000 Ω,
(b) 1000 Ω, (c) 1048 Ω **9.** 71.3 kHz **10.** 0.506 pF

JOB 19-1 Page 663 **1.** (a) 14.4 A, (b) 8.33 Ω,
(c) 1728 W **2.** (a) 0.75 A, (b) 16 Ω, (c) 0, (d) 0 W
3. (a) 1.5 A, (b) 66.7 Ω, (c) 0, (d) 0 W **4.** (a) 3.85 A,
(b) 28.6 Ω, (c) 100%, (d) 423.5 W **5.** 0.11 A;
1636 Ω; 0 W **6.** I_1 = 0.0005 A, I_2 = 0.000 05 A,
I_T = 0.000 55 A, Z = 909 Ω **7.** (a) 0.159 A, 0.064 A,
(b) 0.223 A, (c) 538 Ω, (d) 0, (e) 0 W **8.** (a) 0.05 A,
0.0125 A, (b) 0.0625 A, (c) 800 Ω, (d) 0, (e) 0 W

JOB 19-2 Page 668 **1.** (a) 13 A, (b) 9.23 Ω, (c) 67°,
(d) 38.5%, (e) 600 W **2.** (a) 1.21 A, (b) 99.2 Ω,
(c) 84°, (d) 9.9%, (e) 14.4 W **3.** (a) 2.15 A,
(b) 46.5 Ω, (c) 22°, (d) 93%, (e) 200 W
4. 5%, 100%, yes **5.** 70%, 100%; Yes, but not a good
filter, since it also passes low frequencies

JOB 19-3 Page 673 **1.** R = 7.2 Ω; C = 276 μF
2. R = 28.2 Ω; L = 16 mH **3.** (a) I_T = 13 A,

(b) Z = 9.23 Ω, (c) θ = 67° lag, (d) PF = 38.46%,
(e) W = 1559.87 W, (f) R = 3.55 Ω, C = 312.5 μF
4. (a) 4.12 A, (b) 29.1 Ω, (c) 14° leading, (d) 97.1%,
(e) 480 W, (f) R = 28.2 Ω; C = 376 μF **5.** (a) X_L =
125.6 Ω, X_C = 53 Ω, (b) I_R = 2 A, I_L = 0.8 A,
I_C = 1.89 A, (c) I_T = 2.52 A, (d) Z = 40 Ω, (e) θ =
37° lead, (f) PF = 79.3%, (g) W = 200 W, (h) R =
31.7 Ω, C = 6.4 μF **6.** (a) X_L = 7536 Ω, X_C = 3312 Ω,
(b) I_L = 0.029 A, I_C = 0.066 A, I_R = 0.1 A, (c) 0.106 A,
(d) 2075 Ω, (e) 19° leading, (f) 94.3%, (g) 22 W,
(h) R = 1963 Ω; C = 3.9 μF

JOB 19-4 Page 678 **1.** I_x = 17.32 A, I_y = 10 A
2. I_x = 8.19 A, I_y = 5.74 A **3.** I_x = 10 A, I_y =
−17.32 A **4.** I_x = 5.74 A, I_y = −8.19 A **5.** I_x =
19.32 A, I_y = 17.4 A **6.** I_x = 1.66 A, I_y = 0.70 A
7. I_x = 64.3 mA, I_y = −76.6 mA **8.** I_x = 4.25 A,
I_y = −1.47 A **9.** I_x = 12.69 A, I_y = 5.92 A
10. I_x = 27.37 A, I_y = −14.55 A

JOB 19-5 Page 688 **1.** EMI = electromagnetic
interference; RFI = radio frequency interference
2. Motors, electronic equipment, cellular phones, flu-
orescent lights, solenoids **3.** Radiated EMI; conduct-
ed EMI **4.** A and B **5.** L = open circuits; C = short
circuits **6.** L = shorted out; C = open **7.** Used to
specify EMI filters **8.** Measurements made between a
line and ground **9.** Measurements between two
lines **10.** Frequency at which an inductor or capacitor changes from being a short circuit to an open
circuit

JOB 19-6 Page 700 **1.** (a) 23.4 A, (b) 5.13 Ω,
(c) 35° leading, (d) 2305 W **2.** (a) I_T = 9.12 A,
(b) Z = 10.9 Ω, (c) 21° leading, (d) 850 W
3. (a) 14.1 A, (b) 7.09 Ω, (c) 0°, (d) 1410 W
4. (a) I_T = 2.19 A, (b) 45.7 Ω, (c) 77° leading,
(d) 50 W **5.** (a) 1.8 A, (b) 55.5 Ω, (c) 48° lagging,
(d) 120 W **6.** (a) I_T = 1.39 A, (b) Z = 72 Ω,
(c) 18° leading, (d) 132 W

JOB 19-7 Page 706 **1.** (a) Z = 21.1 Ω, (b) I_T = 4.74
A, (c) θ = 17° lagging, (d) 95.6%, (e) P = 454 W
2. (a) Z = 36.3 Ω, (b) I_T = 2.75 A, (c) 33° leading,
(d) 84%, (e) 231 W **3.** (a) Z = 60.7 Ω,
(b) L_T = 1.98 A, (c) θ = 31° lagging, (d) 85.9%,
(e) P = 204 W **4.** (a) Z = 99 Ω, (b) I_T = 0.50 A,
(c) 27° leading, (d) 89.2%, (e) 22.3 W
5. (a) Z = 30.9 Ω, (b) I_T = 3.9 A, (c) θ = 12° leading,
(d) 97.6%, (e) P = 457 W

JOB 19-8 Page 708 **1.** 5300 kHz **2.** 1987.5 kHz
3. 400 pF **4.** 1193 μH **5.** 80 pF **6.** (a) 0.0101 μF,
(b) 0.00253 μF **7.** 0.92 μH **8.** 2.45 mH **9.** 40.2 pF

JOB 19-9 Page 712 **1.** (a) 0.083 A, (b) 301 Ω,
(c) 0 W **2.** (a) 1.2%, (b) 100%, (c) High-pass

3. (a) $I_R = 0.5$ A, $I_L = 0.16$ A, (b) $I_T = 0.52$ A, (c) 192 Ω, (d) 16°, (e) 96.2%, (f) 50 W
4. (a) $I_R = 0.02$ A, $I_C = 0.314$ A, (b) 0.314 A, (c) 31.8 Ω **5.** (a) 128 mA, (b) 1875 Ω, (c) 51°, (d) 62.5%, (e) 19.2 W **6.** (a) 0.55 A, (b) 400 Ω, (c) 78°, (d) 20%, (e) 24.2 W **7.** (a) 17.1 A, (b) 7 Ω, (c) 31° leading, (d) 85.6%, (e) 1756 W **8.** (a) 0.93 A, (b) 107 Ω, (c) 17°, (d) 95.7%, (e) 89 W **9.** 120 μH
10. 56 pF **11.** (a) 10 Ω, (b) $I_T = 10$ A, (c) 37° leading, (d) 800 W **12.** (a) 4 A, (b) 2 A, (c) 78.1% lagging

JOB 20-1 Page 720 1. 80 percent **2.** 2400 W
3. 360 W **4.** 20,000 VA **5.** (a) 4400 VA, (b) 90.9% **6.** 38.5%, 405 W **7.** 2.5 A **8.** 83.3%
9. 45.45 A **10.** 81.8% **11.** 3450 VA; 2933 W
12. (a) 10,660 Ω, (b) 46.9%, (c) 3.8 mA, (d) 0.06 W
13. 10,417 VA **14.** 16.7 A **15.** 40 A **16.** 1875 W, 78.1% **17.** 800 var **18.** 100 kVA **19.** 10 A **20.** (a) 5500 VA, (b) 4400 W, (c) 3300 var

JOB 20-2 Page 727 1. (a) 1232 W, (b) 80% leading, (c) 1540 VA, (d) 14 A **2.** (a) $PF_A = 72.7\%$, $PF_B = 72.7\%$, (b) 1280 W, (c) 72.7%, (d) 1760 VA, (e) 16 A **3.** (a) 1650 W, (b) 89.9%, (c) 1835 VA, (d) 16.7 A **4.** (a) 1992 W, (b) 98.2%, (c) 2029 VA, (d) 18.4 A **5.** (a) 27 kW, (b) 54.5%, (c) 49.5 kVA
6. (a) 5 kW, (b) 78.8%, (c) 6.35 kVA, (d) 57.7 A
7. (a) 13 kW, (b) 73.1%, (c) 17.8 kVA, (d) 80.9 A
8. (a) 1400 W, (b) 62.9%, (c) 2226 VA, (d) 20.2 A
9. (a) 72 kW, (b) 64.3%, (c) 112 kVA
10. (a) 3036 W, (b) 62.9%, (c) 4827 VA, (d) 21.9 A

JOB 20-3 Page 733 1. (a) 950 W, (b) 99.8%, (c) 952 VA **2.** (a) 141 kW, (b) 99.9%, (c) 141.1 kVA
3. (a) 5680 W, (b) 92.1%, (c) 6167 VA, (d) 51.4 A
4. (a) 2260 W, (b) 99.98%, (c) 2260 VA, (d) 18.8 A
5. 98.8% **6.** (a) 1500 W, (b) 99.8%, (c) 1503 VA, (d) 12.5 A **7.** (a) 22 kW, (b) 90.6%, (c) 24.28 kVA, (d) 105.6 A **8.** (a) 93.4%, (b) 92.1% **9.** (a) 1584 W, (b) 94.6%, (c) 1674 VA, (d) 13.95 A **10.** (a) 1700 W, (b) 99%, (c) 1717 VA, (d) 14.3 A

JOB 20-4 Page 744 1. 17.4% **2.** 80% **3.** 58.8%
4. 240 μF **5.** 38 μF **6.** 481 μF **7.** 6.67 kVA
8. (a) 1.80 kW; 2. 86.6%; 3. 92.4 kVA, (b) 39.1%
9. 109.6 kvar; Graph − 108; 4 standard 25-C kvar, 63.5 kVA released; Graph = 64 kVA **10.** (a) 51.4 C kvar, (b) 23.7 kVA, Graph (a) 52.8 C kvar, (b) 25 kVA **11.** (a) 111.6 kW, (b) 93.3 kvar, (c) 76.6%, (d) 145.7 kVA, (e) (1) 25 C kvar plus, (1) 15 C kvar
12. (a) 126.42 kW, (b) 12.04 kvar, (c) 99.6%, (d) 126.9 kVA

JOB 20-5 Page 747 1. 28%, 4.8 A **2.** (a) 1667 W, (b) 2084 VA **3.** (a) 1944 W, (b) 90%, (c) 2160 VA,

(d) 18 A **4.** (a) 5002 W, (b) 95.1%, (c) 5260 VA, (d) 23.9 A **5.** (a) 22.5 kW, (b) 62.9%, (c) 35.8 kVA
6. (a) 415 W, (b) 94.6%, (c) 439 VA **7.** (a) 1936 W, (b) 99.5%, (c) 1946 VA, (d) 16.6 A **8.** (a) 4623 VA, (b) 20.1 A **9.** 45.4% **10.** (a) 1429 VA, (b) 1027 var, (c) 225 μF **11.** (a) 80%, (b) 900 var, (c) 900 var
12. 60% **13.** (a) 82.4 kVA, (b) 32°, (c) 43.7 kvar, (d) 1-15 C kvar, plus, 1-25 C kvar, (e) 99.9%
14. 34.3 C kvar, 16.3 kVA **15.** 22.6 C kvar; 7.5 kVA released

JOB 21-1 Page 762 1. 2078 V **2.** 2402 V **3.** 40 A
4. 18.29 kW **5.** (a) 460 V, (b) 4505 W, (c) 13.52 kW
6. (a) 61 kVA, (b) 82% **7.** (a) 9.01 kVA, (b) 88%
8. (a) 251 A, (b) 251 A, (c) 1328 V **9.** (a) 4858 kVA, (b) 0.823, (c) 3810 V **10.** 597.5 kVA, (b) 0.837, (c) 1328 V **11.** (a) 12,000 V, (b) 361 A, (c) 7500 kVA, (d) 6000 kW **12.** (a) 10,000 kW, (b) 721.7 A, (c) 5774 V **13.** (a) 6.93 A, (b) 6.93 A, (c) 1440 W
14. (a) 127 V, (b) 12.7 A, (c) 12.7 A, (d) 4839 W
15. (a) 480 V, (b) 13 Ω, (c) 21.3 A, (d) 21.3 A, (e) 0.923, (f) 16.34 kW **16.** (a) 254 V, (b) 100 kVA, (c) 131.2 A, (d) 131.2 A, (e) 60 kvar **17.** (a) 4157 V, (b) 127.4 kW, (c) 20.8 A, (d) 20.8 A
18. (a) 17,500 kVA, (b) 765.5 A, (c) 765.5 A, (d) 7621 V **19.** (a) 100 Ω, (b) 138.6 V, (c) 1.39 A, (d) 0.866, (e) 500 W, (f) 577 VA **20.** (a) 26, (b) 0.923, (c) 9.77 A, (d) 9.77 A, (e) 6872 W, (f) 7.45 kVA

JOB 21-2 Page 769 1. 103.9 A **2.** 28.9 A **3.** 440 V
4. 44 Ω **5.** (a) 5.77 A, (b) 10 A **6.** (a) 120 V, (b) 34.6 A, (c) 7.19 kVA, (d) 5.75 kW **7.** (a) 240 V, (b) 10 A, (c) 17.3 A, (d) 7.2 kW, (e) 7.2 kVA
8. (a) 20 Ω, (b) 0.8, (c) 220 V, (d) 11 A, (e) 19.1 A, (f) 5.82 kW, (g) 7.28 kVA **9.** (a) 0.82, (b) 35°, (c) 61 kVA, (d) 35 kvar **10.** (a) 400 V, (b) 400 V, (c) 40 A, (d) 10 Ω, (e) $R = 8$ Ω, $X = 6$ Ω
11. (a) 72 kVA, (b) 72 kVA **12.** (a) 180.4 A, (b) 240 V, (c) 25 kVA, 104.2 A, 240 V

JOB 21-3 Page 774 1. (a) 17.3 A, (b) 240 V, (c) 12.5 kVA **2.** 6.93 A **3.** 27.4 kW **4.** (a) 208 V, (b) 40 A, (c) 40 A, (d) 14.4 kVA **5.** (a) 350 A, (b) 208 V, (c) 100.8 kW **6.** (a) 606.2 A, (b) 120 V, (c) 100.8 kW **7.** 120 kW **8.** (a) 520 kW, (b) 288.7 A, (c) 288.7 A, (d) 750.6 V **9.** (a) 520 kW, (b) 166.7 A, (c) 288.7 A, (d) 1300 V **10.** (a) 25 Ω, (b) 0.96, (c) 220 V, (d) 8.8 A, (e) 15.24 A, (f) 5.57 kW, (g) 5.8 kVA **11.** (a) 6 A, (b) 1.73 kW, (c) 3.46 A, (d) $R = 16$ Ω, $X_L = 12$ Ω **12.** (a) 32.34 A, (b) 56 A, (c) 208 V **13.** (a) 40.7 kW; 36.8 kvar, (b) 20.0 kVA; 12.0 kvar, (c) 56.7 kW; 24.8 kvar, (d) 0.914, (e) 74.62 A

14. (*a*) 187.5 kW, 164 kvar, (*b*) 80 kW, 60 kvar, (*c*) 267.6 kW, 104 kvar, (*d*) 0.934

JOB 22-3   Page 779   **1.** (*a*) 5, (*b*) 8.7, (*c*) 15, (*d*) 8.7
2. Because the transformer is assumed lossless and the circuits are balanced, the power in all phases is 34.6 kW. Prove it by doing all parts of the problem.
3. All answers are $I = 14.4$ A because the input line voltage and the load power is fixed and the transformer is fixed and the transformer is assumed lossless. Check all of the configurations to see that this is true.   **4.** The secondary line currents are all 125 A. The phase currents are (*a*) 72.2 A, (*b*) 72.2 A, (*c*) 125 A, (*d*) 125 A   **5.** Problem 3 showed that the line currents are all 14.4 A. The phase currents are determined by the delta and wye relationships between line and phase currents. (*a*) 14.4, (*b*) 8.3, (*c*) 8.3, (*d*) 14.4

JOB 23-2   Page 807   **1.** (*a*) 0, (*b*) 1, (*c*) 0
2.

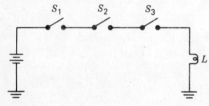

3. $L = S_1 \cdot S_2$ **4.** $L = 0$

JOB 23-3   Page 810   **1.** 8   **2.** 00, 01, 10, 11   **3.** 4
4. 8

JOB 23-4   Page 813   **1.** 1.16

2.

S_1	S_2	S_3	$S_1 \cdot S_2 + S_3$
0	0	0	0
0	0	1	1
0	1	0	0
0	1	1	1
1	0	0	0
1	0	1	1
1	1	0	1
1	1	1	1

3.

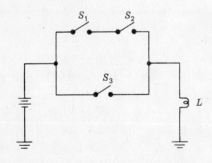

4.

S_1	S_2	$(S_1 S_2)^1$	S_3	$(S_1 S_2)^1 + S_3$
0	0	1	0	1
0	0	1	1	1
0	1	1	0	1
0	1	1	1	1
1	0	1	0	1
1	0	1	1	1
1	1	0	0	0
1	1	0	1	1

5.

S_1	S_2	$(S_1 S_2)'$	$S_1' + S_2'$
0	0	1	1
0	1	1	1
1	0	1	1
1	1	0	0

JOB 23-6   Page 819
1.

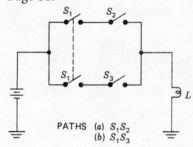

PATHS (*a*) $S_1 S_2$
(*b*) $S_1 S_3$

2.

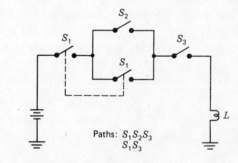

Paths: $S_1 S_2 S_3$
$S_1 S_3$

3.

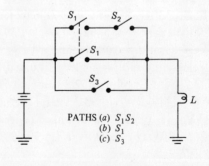

PATHS (*a*) $S_1 S_2$
(*b*) S_1
(*c*) S_3

4. No

5.

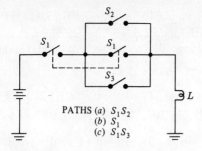

PATHS (a) $S_1 S_2$
(b) S_1
(c) $S_1 S_3$

JOB 23-7   Page 821

1.

S_1'	S_2	S_3	$(S_2 + S_3)$	S_1	L
0	0	0	0	1	1
0	0	1	1	1	1
0	1	0	1	1	1
0	1	1	1	1	1
1	0	0	0	0	0
1	0	1	1	0	1
1	1	0	1	0	1
1	1	1	1	0	1

2.

S_2	S_1	S_1'	S_2'	$S_1 S_2$	$S_1' S_2'$	L
0	0	1	1	0	1	1
0	1	0	1	0	0	0
1	0	1	0	0	0	0
1	1	0	0	1	0	1

3.

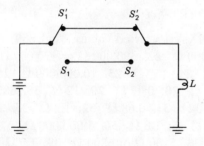

4.

S_1	S_2	$S_1 S_2'$	$S_1' S_2$	L
0	0	0	0	0
0	1	0	1	1
1	0	1	0	1
1	1	0	0	0

5. $L_1 = L_1'$

The user cannot tell the difference in the operation.

6.

S_3	S_2	S_1	S_3'	S_2'	S_1'	L
0	0	0	1	1	1	1
0	0	1	1	1	0	0
0	1	0	1	0	1	0
0	1	1	1	0	0	1
1	0	0	0	1	1	0
1	0	1	0	1	0	1
1	1	0	0	0	1	0
1	1	1	0	0	0	1

JOB 23-8   Page 828

1.

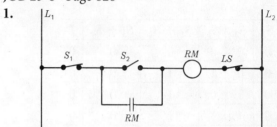

2. There is one path: $S_1 L_S S_2$ **3.** If $R_M = 1$, then $R_M = S_1 L_S$ **4.** Then $R_M = S_1 L_S S_2$, and the motor would not latch on. **5.** (a) If the relay burned shut, then $R_M = S_1 L_S$. (b) Either push S_1 or let the motor run to the limit switch.

JOB 23-9   Page 834

1.

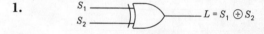

$L = S_1 \oplus S_2$

2.

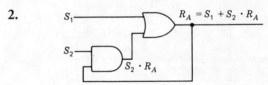

$R_A = S_1 + S_2 \cdot R_A$

3.

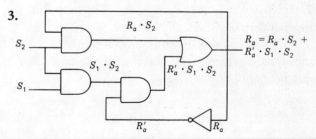

$R_a = R_a \cdot S_2 + R_a' \cdot S_1 \cdot S_2$

4.

S_1	S_2	L
0	0	0
0	1	1
1	0	1
1	1	0

5. $L = S_1(S_2 + S_3)$

S_3	S_2	S_1	$S_2 + S_3$	L
0	0	0	0	0
0	0	1	0	0
0	1	0	1	0
0	1	1	1	1
1	0	0	1	0
1	0	1	1	1
1	1	0	1	0
1	1	1	1	1

6. $L = (S_1 S_2) + S_3$

S_4	S_3	S_2	S_1	$S_1 + S_2$	$S_3 + S_4$	L
0	0	0	0	0	0	0
0	0	0	1	1	0	0
0	0	1	0	1	0	0
0	0	1	1	1	0	0
0	1	0	0	0	1	0
0	1	0	1	1	1	1
0	1	1	0	1	1	1
0	1	1	1	1	1	1
1	0	0	0	0	1	0
1	0	0	1	1	1	1
1	0	1	0	1	1	1
1	0	1	1	1	1	1
1	1	0	0	0	1	0
1	1	0	1	1	1	1
1	1	1	0	1	1	1
1	1	1	1	1	1	1

7. 1; No; since $S_3 = 1$, $S_3 + S_4 = 1$. The output is independent of S_4. **8.** 0. No. Since $S_1 = 0$ and $S_2 = 0$, $S_1 + S_2 = 0$. This means that one of the inputs to AND gate 3 is 0. Therefore the output is a 0 independent of $S_3 + S_4$.

JOB 24-1 Page 843 **1.** (*a*) 0.30103, (*b*) −0.30103, (*c*) −0.30103, (*d*) 1.69897, (*e*) 2.69897, (*f*) −2.39794 **2.** (*a*) 1.778, (*b*) 3.024, (*c*) 0.996, (*d*) 3.041, (*e*) 0.544, (*f*) −3.078

JOB 24-3 Page 847 **1.** −0.58 dB **2.** 0.22 dB **3.** 3.01 dB **4.** 100 **5.** 10 **6.** 17 dB **7.** 63.65 dB

JOB 24-4 Page 851 **1.** (*a*) 11.25 dB, (*b*) 2.47 V **2.** 1.76 dB **3.** (*a*) 57.15 dB, (*b*) 327 ft **4.** 123 ft **5.** 3.47 dB **6.** (*a*) 3 dB, (*b*) 0.5 W, (*c*) At −3 dB the power is ½ the reference power. **7.** (*a*) 3.01 dB, (*b*) 3.01 dB, (*c*) 6.02, (*d*) yes **8.** (*a*) 1,000,000, (*b*) 1000, (*c*) The power ratio is the square of the voltage ratio. (*d*) $P = \dfrac{E^2}{R}$ **9.** (*a*) 60 dB, (*b*) 40.97 dB, (*c*) 100.97 dB

10. 4.73

APPENDIX A: Color Codes Page 857 **1.** 100,000 Ω **2.** 2400 Ω **3.** 82,000 Ω **4.** 5100 Ω **5.** 75 Ω **6.** 2,000,000 Ω **7.** 4.7 Ω **8.** 150,000 Ω **9.** 1.2 Ω **10.** 1200 Ω **11.** 1,800,000 Ω **12.** 0.39 Ω **13.** 620 Ω **14.** 180 Ω **15.** 9100 Ω **16.** 3.3 Ω **17.** 0.47 Ω **18.** 0.45 Ω **19.** 82 Ω **20.** 5.6 Ω **21.** Red, yellow, yellow **22.** Yellow, orange, yellow **23.** Green, brown, black **24.** Brown, green, brown **25.** Brown, black, blue **26.** Green, blue, gold **27.** Orange, white, red **28.** Yellow, violet, silver **29.** Brown, red, black **30.** Violet, green, yellow **31.** Blue, gray, silver **32.** Brown, red, gold **33.** Red, red, gold **34.** Brown, black, brown **35.** Brown, gray, gold **36.** Brown, black, green **37.** Orange, blue, brown **38.** Blue, red, red **39.** Brown, green, gold **40.** Brown, black, gold

APPENDIX A: Preferred Values Page 859 **21.** 220,000 Ω **22.** 390,000 Ω or 470,000 Ω **23.** 47 Ω **24.** 150 Ω **25.** 10,000,000 Ω **26.** 5.6 Ω **27.** 3900 Ω **28.** 0.47 Ω **29.** 12 Ω **30.** 680,000 Ω or 820,000 Ω **31.** 0.68 Ω **32.** 1.2 Ω **33.** 2.2 Ω **34.** 100 Ω **35.** 1.8 Ω **36.** 1,000,000 Ω **37.** 33 Ω or 39 Ω **38.** 5600 Ω or 6800 Ω **39.** 1.5 Ω **40.** 1 Ω

Answers to Textbook Assessments

CHAPTER 1   Page 12   **1.** electromotive force
2. ampere, A   **3.** conductor   **4.** circuit

CHAPTER 2   Page 52   **1.** 34.5 ft   **2.** 5   **3.** 5 V
4. $13.95 each, $180.37   **5.** 0.125, 0.250, 0.375, 0.500,
0.625, 0.750, 0.875   **6.** 106.68 cm   **7.** $25.74

CHAPTER 3   Page 96   **1.** Given the formula $P = E_2/R$,
multiply both sides of the equation by R and $1/P$.
Cancel like variables. The formula becomes $R = E_2/P$.
Substitute the known values for the variables on the
right side of the equation and solve for R: 28.8.
2. $Z = (R)^2 + (X_L - X_C)^2$ **3.** 469.44 yd^3 **4.** 1440 W
5. 162.457 in^3 **6.** 8 A   **7.** 100 V   **8.** 4.125   **9.** 0.625 nF
10. 11.4075 W

CHAPTER 4   Page 134   **1.** 50 V   **2.** 44 V   **3.** 4.7916 V
4. $E_{R_3} = 3.3414$ V   **5.** 1.667 A   **6.** 297.25 mV   **7.** 20
8. 1.92 Ω   **9.** 0 resistance

CHAPTER 5   Page 175   **1.** 11.0139 kΩ   **2.** 0.3333
amperes per lamp, 4.667 A   **3.** One-tenth is the larger
of the two   **4.** 5⅝ in.   **5.** 141¾ lb   **6.** 14.32394 kHz
7. 203.5   **8.** 600 V   **9.** 300 V   **10.** $I_T = 110$ mA +
230 mA + 335 mA = 675 mA, $R_T = E/I_T$, $R_T =$
100 V/0.675 A = 148.148 Ω   **11.** 537.313 Ω

CHAPTER 6   Page 210   **1.** $R_T = 8.184$ Ω, $I_T = 14.662$,
$P_T = 1759.45$ W   **2.** $R_T = 39.047$ kΩ, $I_T = 133.171$ μA
3. $I_T = 10$ A, $E_L = 90$ V, $E_D = 30$ V   **4.** To ensure
that the load will be able to function properly, the
input voltage must be within limits outlined by the
manufacturer. Calculating voltage drop and sizing
conductors appropriately can help guarantee that the
voltage supply to the lead will be correct.

CHAPTER 7   Page 242   **1.** $I_T = 7.708$ A
2. $E_T = 120$ V   **3.** $E_T = 70.71$ V   **4.** 3.1787×10^{-11}
5. $P_{heat} = I^2 \cdot R = 80^2 \cdot 46.875$ mΩ = 300 W
6. 8.5147×10^{-5} F   **7.** 10.6 A

CHAPTER 8   Page 282   **1.** 50.14Xy **2.** $7.2R + 5aB +$
$13T$ **3.** $b = 8$ **4.** $T = 36$ **5.** $-7x + 16y - 10z$
6. $w = 32.842$ **7.** $k = 8.75$ **8.** $45R + 57$ **9.** $X = 1.25$
10. $X = 80$ **11.** $p = 2.75, b = 4.25$

CHAPTER 9   Page 345   **1.** $I_T = 9.708$ mA,
$R_1 = 97.087$ mV, $R_2 = 9.708$ V, $R_3 = 194.17$ mV
2. $I_T = 254.55$ mA   **3.** $X = 1.12$ A, $Y = 1.76$ A,

$Z = 0.64$ A, $R_1 = 3.2$ V, $R_2 = 19.02$ V, $R_3 = 7.84$ V,
$R_4 = 12.32$ V, $R_5 = 8.8$ V, $X\leftarrow$, $Y\rightarrow$, $Z\leftarrow$
4. $E_w = 22.169$ V, $E_v = 20.915$ V, $E_z = 1.2549$ V,
$E_x = 23.843$ V, $E_y = 25.098$ V, applied voltage =
46.013 V   **5.** $R_{TH} = 3.65$ kΩ, $R_{load} = 32$ Ω

6.

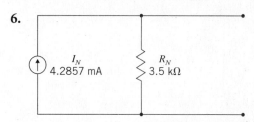

CHAPTER 10   Page 396   **1.** 0.25 Ω   **2.** 45 mA
3. 124.995 Ω   **4.** $E_{R_1} = 441.176$ Ω, $E_{R_2} = 1,041.667$ Ω,
$E_{R_3} = 10,000$ Ω, $E_{R_4} = 13,333$ Ω, $E_{R_5} = 6,500$ Ω,
$E_{R_7} = 2,000$ Ω, $I_T = 200$ mA, $E_T = 400$ V   **5.** 38.636 V
6. The Wheatstone bridge is an instrument used
to obtain accurate measurements of an unknown
resistance.   **7.** Thevenin values reduce the complexity
of circuits for analysis, making the substitution of
load values easier to do without having to reanalyze
each circuit.   **8.** $I_{load} = 3.607$ mA, $E_{load} = 10.82$ V,
$E_C = 4.1799$ V   **9.** $I_{load} = 6$ mA, $E_{load} = 9$ V,
$E_C = -11$ V   **10.** $E_{R_C} = 30$ V   **11.** An attenuator
pad reduces source voltage to voltage required without affecting the current.   **12.** The resistor will heat
up and possibly cause a fire (or at a minimum
become unusable).

CHAPTER 11   Page 418   **1.** (a) 55.95 kW, (b) 25.13
kW, (c) 1,119,000 W   **2.** 83.33%   **3.** 40 hp
4. When load impedance and source impedance are
of equal value, the maximum transfer of power will
occur.

CHAPTER 12   Page 459   **1.** 11.25 in^3 (cubic inches)
2. 6 Ω   **3.** 1.84 Ω   **4.** 5199.29 ft   **5.** 0.15734 Ω/1000 ft
6. 44.596 ft   **7.** 0.101882 in.

CHAPTER 13   Page 475   **1.** (a) 108.978 V, (b) 120 V
2. No. 2 type RH (see Table 13–1)   **3.** 500 MCM

CHAPTER 14   Page 496   **1.** 75.963°   **2.** sin ∠$a =$
0.8 = 53.13°, cos ∠a = 0.6 = 53.13°, tan ∠a = 1.33 =
53.13°, sin ∠b = 0.6 = 36.86°, cos ∠b = 0.8 = 36.86°,
tan ∠b = 0.75 = 36.86°   **3.** 32.005°   **4.** 30.9637°

CHAPTER 15   Page 539   **1.** (*a*) 63.2%, (*b*) 86.45%, (*c*) 95.01%, (*d*) 98.166%, (*e*) 100%   **2.** 0.5 ms
3. An ac peak voltage across a given resistance will not produce the same I^2R heating as will a dc voltage of the same numerical value. The rms or effective voltage is that numerical value of a sine waveform (70.71% of E_{peak}) equal to a dc voltage that produces the same I^2R heating as does the ac voltage. It effectively produces the same I^2R heating action.
4. 400 Hz   **5.** $\longrightarrow$ 120 V $\longrightarrow$ 6 A (*Note:* The two values are not related, and so there is no relationship between the length of their vectors.)
6. 7.416 ft

7.

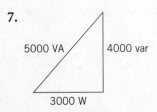

5000 VA   4000 var   3000 W

8. Show a picture of a 60-mHz wave with a 180-Hz wave superimposed on the same graph. Then show the distorted waveform as a result of the fundamental and third harmonic frequency.

CHAPTER 16   Page 603   **1.** 79.577 mH   **2.** (*a*) 50 Ω, (*b*) 79.577 mH, (*c*) 30 Ω, (*d*) 58.3095 Ω, (*e*) 3.43 A, (*f*) 30.9637°, (*g*) 85.749%, (*h*) 588.235 W, (*i*) 353.941 var, (*j*) 685.99 VA   **3.** 99.9968 Ω
4. 338.627 mH   **5.** As the frequency increases, X_L will also increase. Impedance Z will increase and will cause a greater voltage drop in the cable.
6. $E_{primary}$ = 480 V   **7.** 1.2 A   **8.** 31.622:1
9. 3200 Ω   **10.** 260.416 VA

CHAPTER 17   Page 630   **1.** 500 μF   **2.** 4.1 μF
3. 12.7659 μF   **4.** 350 μF   **5.** 109.95 A   **6.** 33 nF
7. (*a*) 40 Ω, (*b*) 17.88 Ω, (*c*) 6 A, (*d*) 3 A, (*e*) 6.708 A, (*f*) 26.568°, (*g*) 89.43% leading, (*h*) 720 VA, (*i*) 260 var, (*j*) 805 VA

CHAPTER 18   Page 656   **1.** (*a*) 50 Ω, (*b*) 111.8 Ω, (*c*) 8.94427 mA, (*d*) 89.4427 V, (*e*) 44.7213 V, (*f*) 25.565°, (*g*) 89.4427% leading, (*h*) 96 W, (*i*) 48 var, (*j*) 107.33 VA   **2.** (*a*) 40 Ω, (*b*) 22.3606 Ω, (*c*) 8.944 A, (*d*) 178.855 V, (*e*) 357.77 V, (*f*) 268.328 V, (*g*) 89.4427%, (*h*) 1600 W, (*i*) 800 var, (*j*) 1788.85 VA, (*k*) 30 Ω
3. 5000 Hz   **4.** 16.887 μH

CHAPTER 19   Page 714   **1.** 7.833 A   **2.** (*a*) 707.84 VA, (*b*) 576 W   **3.** X_L = 65 Ω, X_C = 80 Ω. More current flows through the inductive branch, making the circuit more inductive.   **4.** Determining height of objects, perpendicularity of walls, conduit bending, etc.   **5.** Instrumentation of any kind, analog signal

cable, computer chips, etc.   **6.** **Diagram 1:** (*a*) 5.1226 Ω, (*b*) 23.425 A, (*c*) 34.9319°, (*d*) 81.98%, (*e*) 2304.6 W, (*f*) 147.1195 var, (*g*) 2811.06 VA   **Diagram 2:** (*a*) 10.965 Ω, (*b*) 9.12 A, (*c*) 21.143°, (*d*) 93.2%, (*e*) 850 W, (*f*) 330.438 var, (*g*) 911.97 VA
Diagram 3: (*a*) 10.965 Ω, (*b*) 9.12 A, (*c*) 21.143°, (*d*) 93.2%, (*e*) 850 W, (*f*) 330.438 var, (*g*) 911.97 VA
Diagram 4: (*a*) 45.6764 Ω, (*b*) 2.1893 A, (*c*) 76.798°, (*d*) 22.838%, (*e*) 50 W, (*f*) 213.145 var, (*g*) 218.93 VA
Diagram 5: (*a*) 55.173 Ω, (*b*) 1.8124 A, (*c*) 48.865°, (*d*) 65.78%, (*e*) 119.23 W, (*f*) 136.51 var, (*g*) 181.247 VA   **Diagram 6:** (*a*) 72.016 Ω, (*b*) 1.388 A, (*c*) 18.174°, (*d*) 95.01%, (*e*) 131.93 W, (*f*) 43.312 var, (*g*) 138.857 VA

7. Diagram 1

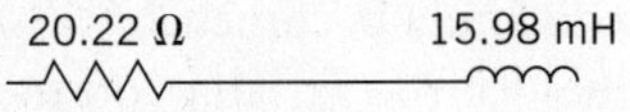

20.22 Ω   15.98 mH

Diagram 2

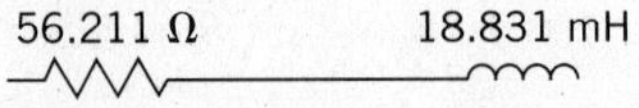

56.211 Ω   18.831 mH

Diagram 3

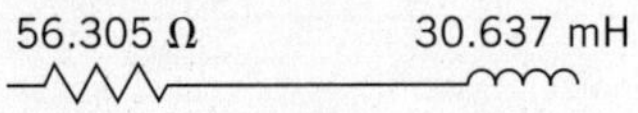

56.305 Ω   30.637 mH

Diagram 4

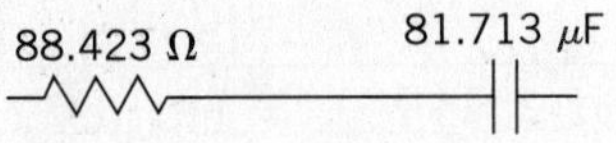

88.423 Ω   81.713 μF

Diagram 5

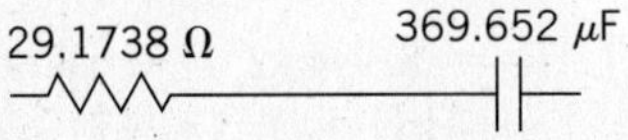

29.1738 Ω   369.652 μF

8. $f = 1/(2\,(\Pi)\,\sqrt{(LC)})$

CHAPTER 20   Page 752   **1.** 62.167%   **2.** AP = 43.517 kVA, TP = 33.84 kW, I_T = 362.65 A
3. AP = 5.911 kVA, PF = 99.8%, I_T = 24.63 A
4. (*a*) 54.05%, (*b*) 11.609 kvar (582.156 μF)

CHAPTER 21   Page 776   **1.** (*a*) 4160 V = 2400 V, (*b*) 8320 V = 4800 V, (*c*) 12,470 V = 7200 V, (*d*) 13,200 V = 7612 V   **2.** 100 kVA available, 4.183 A primary, 23.1495 secondary

CHAPTER 22   Page 801   **1.** Connected kilowatts = 2125   **2.** $I_{primary}$ = 346.96 A, $I_{secondary}$ = 6939.3 A

CHAPTER 23   Page 835

1. L_s P_s F_s

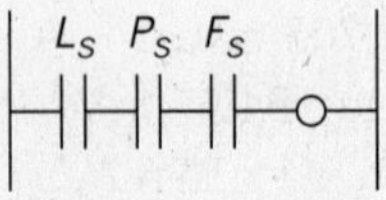

2. 4096 combinations

3.

	LS_1	PS_1	FS_1	HS_1	L_1
1	0	0	0	0	0
2	0	0	1	0	0
3	0	1	0	0	0
4	0	1	1	0	0
5	1	0	0	0	0
6	1	0	1	0	0
7	1	1	0	0	0
8	1	1	1	0	0
9	0	0	0	1	1
10	0	0	1	1	1
11	0	1	0	1	1
12	0	1	1	1	1
13	1	0	0	1	1
14	1	0	1	1	1
15	1	1	0	1	1
16	1	1	1	1	1

4. On a truth table the input variables are arranged in binary number sequence.

5.

	LS_1	PS_1	FS_1	HS_1	L_1
1	0	0	0	0	0
2	0	0	1	0	0
3	0	1	0	0	0
4	0	1	1	0	0

6. It is the result of the action of a single-pole, double-throw switch. Rather than on/off action, the switch becomes position 1 and position 2 (the complement). **7.** Draw the limit switch on the right side of the relay coil on the left side of the relay coil.

CHAPTER 24   Page 852   **1.** A *logarithm* is the exponent (or power) to which a stated number is raised to yield a specific number. For example, $10^2 = 100$. **2.** dB $= 10 \times \log_{10}(12.5/25) = -3.0103$ **3.** dB $= 9 \times (30/100) = 2.7$, $V_1/V_2 = 10^{dB/20} = 0.135$, $V_1(V_{out}) = 3.5 \times 10^{-0.135} = 2.564$ V. Yes; there is less power loss.

Answers to Workbook

JOB 1-1 **1.** An atom is the smallest part of an element that still retains all the characteristics of the element. An atom can be broken down into smaller individual parts, but these parts do not have any of the properties of the element. All matter is made up of combinations of elements that, in turn, are made up of atoms. **2.** An atom contains the following particles: protons, electrons, and neutrons. Protons possess a positive electric charge, and electrons possess a negative electric charge. Neutrons possess no electric charge. **3.** The structure of the atom is such that all protons and neutrons are in the center or nucleus of the atom. The electrons revolve around the nucleus in successive shells or rings. The number of revolving electrons is equal to the number of protons in the nucleus. Fig. 1 shows the structure of a lithium atom.

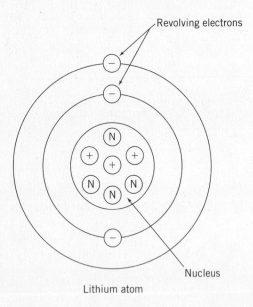

Revolving electrons

Nucleus

Lithium atom

Figure 1

4. For atoms containing more than one orbiting ring of electrons, the outermost ring always requires 8 electrons for maximum electrical stability. Since a copper atom has only 1 electron in its outermost (valence) ring, it is highly unstable. The single electron in the outermost ring is bound very loosely to the nucleus and can move easily from atom to atom within a copper wire. Because it can move freely from one atom to the next, it is called a *free electron*.

5. *Voltage* can be defined as the electrical pressure or force that moves electrons along a wire. The unit of voltage is the volt (V). **6.** 1 coulomb (C) of electricity contains 6 billion billion electrons. **7.** Current can be described as the flow of electrons in an electric circuit. The unit of current is the ampere (A). A current of 1 A represents a flow of 6 billion billion (1 C) electrons past a point in a wire in 1 second (s).
8. Resistance can be defined as the opposition a circuit offers to the flow of current. The unit of resistance is the ohm (Ω). **9.** A conductor is a material in which electrons can travel freely. An insulator is a material that prevents electrons from traveling through it freely. **10.** The symbol for voltage is V, the symbol for current is I, and the symbol for resistance is R.

JOB 1-2 **1.** An ammeter must be connected directly into the circuit so that all the moving electrons can pass through it. See Fig. 2. The resistance of an amme-

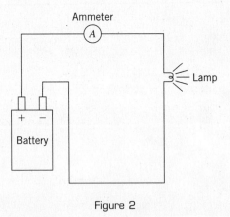

Ammeter

Lamp

Battery

Figure 2

ter must be very low so that it does not stop the flow of current. **2.** A voltmeter must have its leads connected across the ends of a component to measure its voltage. See Fig. 3. **3.** Like a voltmeter, an ohmmeter is connected across the ends of a component to measure its resistance. All power must be off in the circuit when an ohmmeter is being used to measure resistance. **4.** A complete circuit provides an unbroken path along which electrons can travel. An open circuit has a break or interruption in the path of traveling electrons. No current can flow in an open circuit.

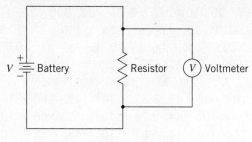

Figure 3

5. A fuse is used to protect a circuit from excessively high currents that may exist as a result of a short somewhere in the circuit. If the short-circuit current exceeds the current rating of the fuse, the fuse will blow and reduce the current to zero, thus protecting the circuit. **6.** When a fuse blows, an open circuit is created. The blown fuse provides a break in the path of moving electrons. **7.** A fuse will blow if the current passing through it exceeds its rated current value. **8.** A delayed fuse is a fuse that can carry approximately twice its rated current for 20 to 30 s before blowing. **9.** See Fig. 4a to j.

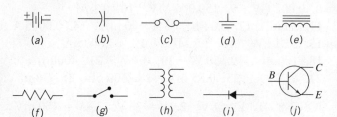

Figure 4

10. (a) a voltage source (b) an unbroken (complete) path for current flow (c) a resistance (or load) to limit current flow (d) a device to start and stop the current flow—such as a switch **11.** See Fig. 5.

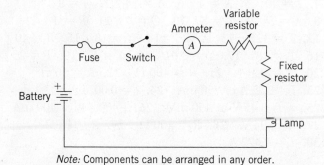

Note: Components can be arranged in any order.

Figure 5

JOBS 2-1 AND 2-2 **1.** $\frac{1}{8}$ **2.** $\frac{3}{8}$ **3.** $\frac{1}{3}$ **4.** $\frac{4}{5}$

5. $\frac{2}{3}$ **6.** $\frac{3}{4}$ **7.** $\frac{9}{16}$ **8.** $\frac{7}{10}$ **9.** $\frac{1}{4}$ **10.** $\frac{1}{11}$ **11.** $\frac{27}{8}$

12. $\frac{67}{9}$ **13.** $\frac{55}{4}$ **14.** $\frac{27}{5}$ **15.** $\frac{13}{4}$ **16.** $\frac{14}{6}$ **17.** $\frac{19}{3}$

18. $\frac{3}{2}$ **19.** $\frac{273}{9}$ **20.** $\frac{101}{7}$ **21.** $5\frac{1}{2}$ **22.** $1\frac{1}{2}$ **23.** $4\frac{1}{2}$

24. $7\frac{1}{3}$ **25.** 15 **26.** $8\frac{1}{3}$ **27.** $7\frac{1}{4}$ **28.** $9\frac{1}{6}$

29. $15\frac{3}{4}$ **30.** $2\frac{3}{16}$ **31.** $\frac{3}{16}$ **32.** $\frac{1}{8}$ **33.** 8 **34.** $18\frac{3}{4}$

35. $\frac{1}{4}$ **36.** 9 **37.** $\frac{1}{9}$ **38.** 2 **39.** 1 **40.** $\frac{8}{9}$

41. $8\frac{8}{9}$ **42.** $19\frac{5}{6}$ **43.** $44\frac{1}{3}$ **44.** $19\frac{29}{32}$ **45.** $3\frac{1}{16}$

46. $7\frac{1}{32}$ **47.** $3\frac{33}{40}$ **48.** $2\frac{22}{25}$ **49.** 15 **50.** $3\frac{15}{16}$

51. $\frac{1}{3}$ **52.** $\frac{2}{9}$ **53.** $\frac{3}{5}$ **54.** $\frac{1}{6}$ **55.** $\frac{1}{70}$ **56.** $1\frac{7}{8}$ A

57. 9 A **58.** 6 V **59.** $133\frac{1}{3}$ ft **60.** $3\frac{3}{4}$ A

61. $51\frac{2}{3}$ dollars **62.** $5\frac{5}{8}$ kWh **63.** $63\frac{3}{8}$ ft. **64.** $\frac{5}{8}$ A

65. 70 V

JOB 2-3 **1.** $V = 200$ V **2.** $V = 25$ V **3.** $V = 16$ V
4. $V = 12$ V **5.** $V = 24$ V **6.** $V = 9.4$ V
7. $V = 27$ V **8.** $V = 2.04$ V **9.** $V = 420$ V
10. $V = 3.75$ V **11.** $V = 37.5$ V **12.** $V = 66$ V
13. $V = 3$ V **14.** $V = 2.2$ V **15.** $V = 3.06$ V
16. $V = 60$ V **17.** $V = 5.4$ V **18.** $V = 2880$ V
19. $V = 120$ V **20.** $V = 14$ V **21.** $V = 10$ V
22. $V = 21$ V **23.** $V = 12$ V **24.** $V = 110$ V
25. $V = 120$ V

JOBS 2-4 AND 2-5 **1.** 0.040 **2.** 0.25 **3.** 0.7
4. 0.066 **5.** 0.20 **6.** 0.15 **7.** 0.3 **8.** 0.02
9. 0.007 **10.** 0.180 **11.** 0.45, 0.15, 0.015
12. 0.9, 0.86, 0.04 **13.** 0.1, 0.099, 0.01
14. 0.27, 0.269, 0.099 **15.** 0.8, 0.75, 0.08 **16.** 5.3
17. 21.077 **18.** 12.092 **19.** 94.13 **20.** 100.006
21. 3.1 **22.** 19.6 **23.** 25.3 **24.** 43.02 **25.** 15.2
26. 0.875 **27.** 0.857 **28.** 0.923 **29.** 0.25
30. 0.4 **31.** 0.375 **32.** 0.375 **33.** 0.5 **34.** 0.167
35. 0.75 **36.** 0.4375 **37.** 3.9375 **38.** 0.59375

39. 4.25 **40.** 8.453125 **41.** $\frac{31}{64}$ **42.** $\frac{13}{16}$ **43.** $\frac{19}{64}$

44. $\frac{63}{64}$ **45.** $\frac{15}{16}$ **46.** $\frac{11}{16}$ **47.** $2\frac{15}{32}$ **48.** $7\frac{9}{16}$

49. $5\frac{19}{64}$ **50.** $\frac{11}{32}$ **51.** 75-W light bulb

52. 0.125 in. long by 0.0625 in. wide **53.** 1.4375 in.

54. $\frac{6}{32}$ in. (aluminum wire) **55.** 6.40625 Ω
(silver wire)

JOB 2-6 **1.** 163 **2.** 40,200 **3.** 0.085 **4.** 2,260,000
5. 105 **6.** 47 **7.** 2.25 **8.** 175,000 **9.** 33,650
10. 0.5 **11.** 0.016 **12.** 250 **13.** 2630 **14.** 0.415

15. 240,000 16. 2.56 17. 4.7 18. 85
19. 0.00247 20. 5.1 21. 0.06 22. 0.000012
23. 0.21 24. 0.0001 25. 0.005 26. 0.01
27. 0.001 28. 0.00056 29. 0.025 30. 0.105
31. 0.5 dm 32. 150 cm 33. 1 km 34. 0.00168 km
35. 1,000 cm 36. 50 cm 37. 250 mm
38. 1.405 km 39. 500,000 mm 40. 450 m
41. 310,000 cm 42. 50 m 43. 5.5 dam
44. 100,000 m 45. 200 m 46. 1.49 MHz
47. 2000 cm 48. 0.025 m 49. 40 m
50. 2,000,000 mm

JOB 2-7 1. 19 2. 12.141 3. 6.49 4. 13.2
5. 11.42 6. 5.17 7. 11.77 8. 11.7 9. 12.48
10. 31.631 11. 3 12. 80 13. 56.95 14. 10.08
15. 0.924 16. 4 17. 8.25 18. 5.07 19. 5
20. 22.55 21. 0.013 Ω 22. 3.45 V 23. 0.2 A
24. $I_T = 7.39$ A 25. $I_1 = 0.55$ A

JOBS 3-1 AND 3-2 1. $R_T = \dfrac{V_A}{I_1 + I_2}$

2. $V_T = I(R_1 + R_2 + R_3)$ 3. $Q = CV$

4. $I_{SH} = I_T - I_M$ 5. $I = \dfrac{V_S - V_Z}{R_S}$ 6. $R_{unk} = \dfrac{RR_T}{R - R_T}$

7. $R_X = R_S \times \dfrac{R_1}{R_2}$ 8. $V_C = V_{CC} - I_C R_C$

9. $L = \dfrac{X_L}{2\pi f}$ 10. $L_T = L_1 + L_2 + 2L_m$ 11. 10

12. 50 13. 65 14. 83 15. 80 16. 12.25
17. 20 18. 3.2 19. 20 20. 9 21. $I = 6.25$ A
22. $I_T = 6$ A 23. $V = 18$ V 24. $I = 0.00005$ A
25. $R_X = 150\ \Omega$ 26. $R_T = 200\ \Omega$ 27. $r_i = 4\ \Omega$
28. $X_L = 3140\ \Omega$ 29. $X_C = 3.18\ \Omega$ 30. $V_{CE} = 7.5$ V

JOB 3-3 1. +20 db 2. −6 db 3. −1000 ft
4. −$500 5. +10 A 6. +100 V 7. −20 mph
8. −30° 9. −5 A 10. −10 μC 11. +40
12. −40 13. −3 14. +50 15. −51 16. +109
17. +5 18. −37 19. −9 20. −25 21. −7
22. +5 23. +100 24. −48 25. 0
26. +72 27. −39 28. +150 P 29. +54
30. −21 A 31. −64 32. +48 33. +36
34. +64 35. −105 36. +12 37. −20
38. −20 39. +5 40. +5b 41. +7g 42. −0.5
43. −3 44. +5 45. −0.25

JOBS 3-4 AND 3-5 1. $A_P = 2250$ 2. $A = 3.14$
in. 3. $Z_P = 800\ \Omega$ 4. $Z_S = 111\ \Omega$ 5. $A = 0.005$
A 6. $P = 0.5$ W 7. $P = 8$ W 8. $R = 144\ \Omega$
9. $R = 240\ \Omega$ 10. $P_T = 1770$ W

JOB 3-6 1. 330 2. 470 3. 15,350 4. 4,700,000
5. 0.68 6. 1800 7. 0.27 8. 3460 9. 1000
10. 39 11. 25 12. 0.0476 13. 66.7 14. 0.75
15. 0.022 16. 0.0039 17. 0.036 18. 17

19. 740 20. 10 21. 0.0025 22. 350 23. 47.6
24. 0.00015 25. 0.00065 26. 0.150 27. 22.5
28. 0.00035 29. 0.0666 30. 0.075 31. 10,000
32. 25,000 33. 476,000 34. 450 35. 100
36. 50 37. 2,250,000 38. 65,200 39. 36
40. 15,500,000 41. 3.65×10^2 42. 6.00×10^3
43. 1.50×10^4 44. 4.76×10^5 45. 1.50×10^6
46. 2.22×10^2 47. 5.67×10^1 48. 6.88×10^1
49. 7.50×10^7 50. 1.12×10^3 51. 1.80×10^{-1}
52. 4.70×10^{-4} 53. 5.00×10^{-2} 54. 1.60×10^{-3}
55. 5.50×10^{-6} 56. 2.00×10^{-2} 57. 3.30×10^{-3}
58. 5.60×10^{-4} 59. 8.80×10^{-10} 60. 1.0×10^{-3}
61. 600,000 or 6.0×10^5 62. 1500 or 1.5×10^3
63. 1,000,000 or 1.0×10^6 64. 30 or 3.0×10^1
65. 6000 or 6.0×10^3 66. 30,000,000 or 3.0×10^7
67. 10^5 or 100,000 68. 450,000 or 4.5×10^5
69. 0.125 or 1.25×10^{-1} 70. 1 71. 10^9 72. 10^7
73. 300 or 3.0×10^2 74. 2400 or 2.4×10^3 75. 2
76. 10^{-2} 77. 10^4 78. 200,000 or 2.0×10^5
79. 40 or 4.0×10^2 80. 10,000 or 1.0×10^4

JOB 3-7 1. 0.0025 A 2. 2,200 kΩ 3. 0.22 MΩ
4. 5,500 W 5. 5 mV 6. 0.25 mA 7. 80,000 μA
8. 0.002 GV 9. 150,000 MV 10. 0.1 μF
11. 20 nF 12. 0.04 μF 13. 100 mA 14. 0.0045 A
15. 65.1 kW 16. 3.5 MHz 17. 65,000 pA
18. 100 nF 19. 50 W 20. 0.3 W 21. 4000 μA
22. 0.025 A 23. 0.55 mV 24. 600 pF 25. 36 μV

JOB 3-8 1. $V = 1$ V 2. $V = 36$ V 3. $V = 150$ mV
4. $V = 150$ V 5. $V = 27$ V 6. $V = 11$ V
7. $V = 2$ V 8. $V = 75$ V 9. $V = 300$ V
10. $V = 330$ mV 11. $R_T = 720\ \Omega$ 12. $P = 1.92$ kW
13. $V = 5.4$ V 14. $I = 500\ \mu$A 15. $R = 15\ \Omega$
16. $V = 0.75$ mV 17. $P = 75\ \mu$W 18. $T = 1.5$ ms
19. $R_T = 35$ kΩ 20. $I_T = 25$ mA

JOB 3-9 1. $X = 9$ 2. $P = 13$ 3. $X = 12$
4. $I = 20$ 5. $X = 2$ 6. $A = 24$ 7. $C = 8$
8. $X = 5$ 9. $X = 8$ 10. $Q = 9$ 11. $R = 4$
12. $F = 125$ 13. $X = 5$ 14. $X = 18$ 15. $B = 40$
16. $L = 18$ 17. $X = 0.01$ 18. $X = 6$ 19. $P = 25$
20. $X = 0.167$ 21. $R = 400\ \Omega$ 22. $R = 30\ \Omega$
23. $I = 0.25$ A or 250 mA 24. $I = 0.0024$ A or 2.4 mA
25. $V = 0.45$ V or 450 mV 26. $I = 0.4$ A or 400 mA
27. $V = 94$ V 28. $R = 400\ \Omega$ 29. $R = 15\ \Omega$
30. $I = 4.472$ A

JOBS 4-1 TO 4-3 1. $R_T = 25\ \Omega$, $I_1 = I_2 = I_T = 3$ A,
$V_1 = 45$ V, $V_2 = 30$ V 2. $R_T = 30\ \Omega$, $I_1 = I_T = 4$ A,
$V_1 = 48$ V, $V_2 = 72$ V, $V_T = 120$ V 3. $R_T = 600\ \Omega$,
$I_2 = I_T = 0.05$ A, $V_1 = 13.5$ V, $V_2 = 16.5$ V, $V_T = 30$ V
4. $R_T = 800\ \Omega$, $I_1 = I_T = 0.03$ A, $V_1 = 20.4$ V,

$V_2 = 3.6$ V, $V_T = 24$ V   **5.** $R_T = 2000$ Ω, $I_1 = I_2 = I_T = 0.025$ A, $V_2 = 40$ V, $V_T = 50$ V   **6.** $R_T = 600$ Ω, $I_1 = I_2 = I_3 = I_T = 0.06$ A, $V_1 = 6$ V, $V_2 = 18$ V, $V_3 = 12$ V   **7.** $R_T = 700$ Ω, $I_1 = I_2 = I_3 = I_T = 0.12$ A, $V_1 = 30$ V, $V_2 = 18$ V, $V_3 = 36$ V   **8.** $R_T = 7500$ Ω, $I_1 = I_3 = I_T = 0.02$ A, $V_1 = 30$ V, $V_2 = 20$ V, $V_3 = 100$ V, $V_T = 150$ V   **9.** $R_T = 18$ Ω, $I_1 = I_2 = I_T = 3$ A, $V_1 = 18$ V, $V_2 = 9$ V, $V_3 = 27$ V, $V_T = 54$ V   **10.** $R_T = 100$ Ω, $I_1 = I_2 = I_3 = I_T = 0.24$ A, $V_2 = 10.8$ V, $V_3 = 4.8$ V, $V_T = 24$ V   **11.** $I_2 = I_3 = I_T = 0.2$ A, $R_1 = 120$ Ω, $R_2 = 90$ Ω, $R_3 = 40$ Ω, $R_T = 250$ Ω, $V_T = 50$ V   **12.** $I_1 = I_2 = I_3 = I_T = 2$ A, $R_1 = 15$ Ω, $V_3 = 100$ V, $R_T = 75$ Ω, $V_T = 150$ V   **13.** $I_1 = I_2 = I_T = 0.015$ A, $V_1 = 13.5$ V, $R_2 = 2000$ Ω, $V_3 = 6$ V, $V_T = 49.5$ V   **14.** $I_1 = I_2 = I_3 = 0.24$ A, $R_1 = 35$ Ω, $V_2 = 3.6$ V, $R_3 = 10$ Ω, $V_T = 14.4$ V, $R_T = 60$ Ω **15.** $I_1 = I_2 = I_3 = 0.05$ A, $V_1 = 75$ V, $V_2 = 12.5$ V, $R_3 = 750$ Ω, $V_T = 125$ V, $R_T = 2500$ Ω **16.** $I_1 = I_2 = I_3 = I_4 = I_T = 10$ mA, $V_1 = 12$ V, $V_2 = 22$ V, $V_3 = 68$ V, $V_4 = 18$ V   **17.** $I_1 = I_2 = I_4 = I_T = 150$ mA, $R_1 = 400$ Ω, $R_2 = 300$ Ω, $V_3 = 30$ V, $V_4 = 15$ V, $R_T = 1000$ Ω or 1 kΩ, $V_T = 150$ V   **18.** $I_1 = I_2 = I_3 = I_4 = I_5 = 250$ μA, $V_1 = 2.5$ V, $R_2 = 20$ kΩ, $R_3 = 50$ kΩ, $V_4 = 1.25$ V, $V_5 = 3.75$ V, $R_T = 100$ kΩ, $V_T = 25$ V   **19.** $V_T = 45$ V   **20.** $V_T = 120$ V   **21.** $R_2 = 80$ Ω **22.** $R_T = 160$ Ω **23.** $I_T = 818.2$ μA, $R_T = 12.2$ kΩ, $V_1 = 8.2$ V, $V_T = 10$ V   **24.** $V_1 = 15$ V, $R_T = 1.92$ kΩ, $V_T = 24$ V   **25.** $R_T = 8$ kΩ, $I_T = 4.5$ mA, $V_T = 36$ V   **26.** Each bulb has a resistance of 25 Ω, $V_T = 120$ V, $R_T = 375$ Ω **27.** 900 Ω **28.** 0.5 mA   **29.** 10 mA   **30.** 20 mA

JOBS 4-4 TO 4-6   **1.** $I_1 = 6$ A, $I_2 = 4$ A, $I_N = 2$ A   **2.** $I_1 = 2$ A, $I_2 = 1.5$ A, $I_N = 0.5$ A   **3.** $I_1 = 3$ A, $I_2 = 3$ A, $I_N = 0$ A   **4.** $I_1 = 4$ A, $I_2 = 1$ A, $I_N = 3$ A   **5.** $I_1 = 8$ A, $I_2 = 12$ A, $I_N = 4$ A   **6.** $I_1 = 20$ A, $I_2 = 30$ A, $I_N = 10$ A   **7.** $I_1 = 15$ A, $I_2 = 15$ A, $I_N = 0$ A   **8.** $I_1 = 3$ A, $I_2 = 2$ A, $I_N = 1$ A   **9.** $I_1 = 12$ A, $I_2 = 18$ A, $I_3 = 6$ A, $I_N = 6$ A   **10.** $I_1 = 15$ A, $I_2 = 14$ A, $I_3 = 12$ A, $I_N = 1$ A   **11.** $I_1 = 8$ A, $I_2 = 7$ A, $I_3 = 4$, $I_N = 1$ A   **12.** $I_1 = 24$ A, $I_2 = 24$ A, $I_3 = 12$ A, $I_N = 0$ A   **13.** $I_1 = 8$ A, $I_2 = 26$ A, $I_3 = 2$ A, $I_N = 18$ A   **14.** $I_1 = 12$ A, $I_2 = 12$ A, $I_3 = 8$ A, $I_N = 0$ A   **15.** $I_1 = 7.5$ A, $I_2 = 8$ A, $I_3 = 6$ A, $I_N = 0.5$ A   **16.** The letters *GFCI* stand for grand-fault circuit-interrupter. It is a special device that detects an imbalance between the currents in the lines carrying current to a load. When the imbalance is about 5 mA, the GFCI opens and thus disconnects power from the load. An imbalance in line currents can be caused by a ground fault from the load to the case or equipment

housing.   **17.** $I_T = 125$ mA, $V_1 = 12.5$ V, $V_2 = 7.5$ V, $R_T = 400$ Ω, $V_T = 50$ V   **18.** $V_1 = 3.2$ V, $V_2 = 12.8$ V, $V_T = 16$ V, $R_T = 10$ kΩ **19.** $V_T = 15$ V   **20.** $R_1 = R_2 = R_3 = 800$ Ω

JOBS 4-7 AND 4-8   **1.** $X = 12$ **2.** $P = 15$ **3.** $X = 17$ **4.** $X = 6$ **5.** $Q = 91$ **6.** $L = 12$ **7.** $Z = 38$ **8.** $Z = 2$ **9.** $M = 54$ **10.** $F = 3$ **11.** $A = 42$ **12.** $B = 86$ **13.** $Q = 10$ **14.** $X = 22$ **15.** $L = 47$ **16.** $d = 474$ **17.** $I = 5\frac{1}{4}$ **18.** $P = 3\frac{7}{8}$ **19.** $C = 16.2$ **20.** $A = 19$ **21.** $X = 56$ **22.** $V = 87$ **23.** $A = 137$ **24.** $X = 14.1$ **25.** $R = 145$ **26.** $Q = 88$ **27.** $G = 21$ **28.** $H = 62$ **29.** $I = 33\frac{1}{4}$ **30.** $X = 50$ **31.** $B = 41$ **32.** $X = 18$ **33.** $B = 133$ **34.** $Z = 90$ **35.** $Y = 19$ **36.** $L = 7$ **37.** $I = 30$ **38.** $C = 5$ **39.** $X = 20$ **40.** $A = 99$ **41.** $V_2 = 5.3$ V   **42.** $I_1 = 4.5$ A   **43.** $P_3 = 125$ mW   **44.** $C_2 = 0.0007$ F   **45.** $L_M = 10$ mH   **46.** $L_M = 125$ μH   **47.** $r_m = 2$ kΩ **48.** $I_M = 0.05$ mA or 50 μA   **49.** $R_2 = 2.4$ kΩ **50.** $C_1 = 0.0015$ μF

JOBS 4-9 AND 4-10   **1.** $I_T = 200$ mA, $R_T = 30$ Ω, $R_1 = 18$ Ω, $V_1 = 3.6$ V   **2.** $I_T = 45$ mA, $R_T = 400$ Ω, $R_2 = 300$ Ω, $V_2 = 13.5$ V   **3.** $V_2 = 16$ V, $I_T = 20$ mA, $R_T = 1.8$ kΩ, $R_1 = 1$ kΩ **4.** $R_1 = 82$ Ω, $V_1 = 12.3$ V, $V_2 = 2.7$ V, $V_T = 15$ V   **5.** $I_T = 25$ mA, $V_T = 30$ V, $V_2 = 10$ V, $V_3 = 17$ V, $R_2 = 400$ Ω **6.** $R_1 = 600$ Ω, $R_3 = 400$ Ω, $R_T = 1.2$ kΩ, $V_2 = 6$ V, $V_T = 36$ V   **7.** $R_T = 4.5$ kΩ, $R_3 = 2$ kΩ, $V_1 = 20$ V, $V_2 = 30$ V, $V_3 = 40$ V   **8.** $V_1 = 40$ V, $I_T = 400$ mA, $R_T = 300$ Ω, $R_2 = 50$ Ω, $R_3 = 150$ Ω **9.** $R_2 = 60$ Ω, $I_T = 200$ mA, $V_T = 24$ V, $V_1 = 4$ V, $V_3 = 2$ V, $V_4 = 6$ V   **10.** $R_T = 20$ kΩ, $R_4 = 9$ kΩ, $V_1 = 1.5$ V, $V_2 = 6$ V, $V_3 = 9$ V, $V_4 = 13.5$ V, $R_4 = 9$ kΩ **11.** 45 Ω **12.** 250 Ω **13.** 10 Ω **14.** 360 Ω **15.** 234 V

JOBS 5-1 AND 5-2   **1.** $I_T = 8$ A, $V_1 = V_2 = 12$ V, $R_T = 1.5$ Ω **2.** $I_T = 15$ A, $V_1 = V_2 = 120$ V, $R_T = 8$ Ω **3.** $I_T = 4$ A, $V_T = 10$ V, $R_T = 2.5$ Ω **4.** $I_T = 75$ mA, $V_1 = V_T = 18$ V, $R_T = 240$ Ω **5.** $I_T = 500$ mA, $V_T = V_1 = V_3 = 90$ V, $R_T = 180$ Ω **6.** $I_T = 3$ A, $V_1 = V_2 = V_3 = 15$ V, $R_T = 5$ Ω **7.** $V_T = V_1 = V_2 = V_3 = 60$ V, $I_2 = 3$ A, $I_T = 5$ A, $R_3 = 120$ Ω, $R_T = 12$ Ω **8.** $V_T = V_1 = V_3 = 12$ V, $I_1 = 1.2$ A, $I_2 = 300$ mA, $R_3 = 8$ Ω, $I_T = 3$ A, $R_T = 4$ Ω **9.** $V_T = V_2 = V_3 = 24$ V, $I_1 = 200$ mA, $I_2 = 400$ mA, $I_T = 1.2$ A, $R_3 = 40$ Ω, $R_T = 20$ Ω **10.** $V_T = V_1 = V_2 = V_3 = 9$ V, $R_1 = 30$ Ω, $I_2 = 450$ mA, $I_T = 900$ mA, $R_T = 10$ Ω **11.** waffle maker: $R = 24$ Ω, 4 light bulbs: $R = 60$ Ω, microwave: $R = 17.1$ Ω, dishwasher: $R = 15$ Ω, toaster: $R = 13.3$ Ω **12.** $I_T = 17$ A,

$R_T = 7.06\ \Omega$ **13.** $I_T = 14$ A, $R_T = 8.57\ \Omega$ **14.** yes **15.** no **16.** (a) $I_T = 3.75$ A (b) 120 V (c) $R_T = 32\ \Omega$ **17.** (a) 120 V, (b) $I_T = 13.1$ A, (c) $R_T = 9.16\ \Omega$ **18.** $V_T = 36$ V, $I_T = 6$ A, $R_T = 6\ \Omega$ **19.** 24 light bulbs **20.** $V_T = V_1 = V_3 = 15$ V, $I_1 = 100$ mA, $I_3 = 150$ mA, $I_T = 300$ mA, $R_T = 50\ \Omega$ **21.** In a series circuit, the current through each component is the same even though the individual voltages in the circuit may be different. In a parallel circuit, the voltage across each component is the same even though the current through each component may be different. **22.** (a) $R_T = 24\ \Omega$ (b) $R_T = 17.1\ \Omega$ (c) $R_T = 8.57\ \Omega$ As more branches are connected to the 120-V line, the total current I_T increases. Since V_T remains the same, the ratio V_T/I_T (which equals R_T) must decrease as more branches are added.

JOBS 5-3 TO 5-5 **1.** $\frac{7}{12}$ **2.** $\frac{8}{9}$ **3.** $\frac{3}{4}$ **4.** $\frac{11}{15}$ **5.** $\frac{7}{8}$

6. $\frac{23}{24}$ **7.** $\frac{13}{20}$ **8.** $\frac{57}{72}$ **9.** $\frac{15}{16}$ **10.** $\frac{311}{396}$ **11.** $1\frac{23}{100}$

12. $1\frac{1}{18}$ **13.** $1\frac{5}{7}$ **14.** $10\frac{1}{8}$ **15.** $7\frac{7}{36}$ **16.** $\frac{5}{8}$

17. $\frac{5}{16}$ **18.** $\frac{2}{7}$ **19.** 0 **20.** $\frac{1}{9}$ **21.** $\frac{16}{39}$ **22.** $\frac{3}{20}$

23. $\frac{4}{21}$ **24.** $\frac{23}{77}$ **25.** $\frac{16}{75}$ **26.** $\frac{1}{3}$ **27.** $3\frac{5}{12}$

28. $11\frac{13}{36}$ **29.** $1\frac{5}{6}$ **30.** $2\frac{9}{56}$ **31.** $I_T = 7\frac{41}{84}$ A

32. $1\frac{1}{8}$ A **33.** $14\frac{5}{24}$ V **34.** $1\frac{15}{32}$ in. **35.** $4\frac{131}{144}$ in.

36. $\frac{1}{16}$ in. **37.** $6\frac{7}{8}$ ft **38.** no **39.** $8\frac{11}{16}$ V

40. $3\frac{19}{24}$ A

JOBS 5-6 AND 5-7 **1.** $X = 36$ **2.** $a = 45$ **3.** $Q = 12$ **4.** $X = 112$ **5.** $L = 162$ **6.** $X = 432$ **7.** $B = 125$ **8.** $C = 6$ **9.** $C = 21$ **10.** $X_L = 500$ **11.** $X = 2.25$ **12.** $X = 4.5$ **13.** $X = 4.5$ **14.** $b = 13.33$ **15.** $X = 15$ **16.** $a = 8.57$ **17.** $X = 0.5$ **18.** $B = 1$ **19.** $X = 8.67$ **20.** $C = 10$ **21.** $P = 15$ **22.** $X = 13.33$ **23.** $a = 22$ **24.** $X = 60$ **25.** $C = 0.05$ **26.** $X = 8$ **27.** $R = 24$ **28.** $R = 0.15$ **29.** $V = 12.8$ **30.** $P = 6.67$ **31.** $V = 120$ **32.** $X_L = 120$ **33.** $Z = 70.7$ **34.** $V_S = 6$ **35.** $I_P = 0.6$ **36.** $V_1 = 9$ V **37.** $R_T = 800\ \Omega$ **38.** $I_1 = 7.2$ A **39.** $R_2 = 10$ kΩ **40.** $R_X = 67.2$ kΩ

JOBS 5-8 TO 5-11 **1.** $R_T = 6\ \Omega$ **2.** $R_T = 15\ \Omega$ **3.** $R_T = 75\ \Omega$ **4.** $R_1 = 40\ \Omega$ **5.** $R_T = 10\ \Omega$ **6.** $R_T = 18\ \Omega$ **7.** $R_T = 40\ \Omega$ **8.** $R_3 = 36\ \Omega$ **9.** $R_T = 150\ \Omega$ **10.** $R_T = 833\frac{1}{3}\ \Omega$ **11.** $V_T = 30$ V **12.** $V_T = 12$ V **13.** $V_T = 18$ V **14.** $V_T = 16$ V **15.** $V_T = 36$ V **16.** 1 kΩ **17.** 15 **18.** 1.5 kΩ

19. $R_3 = 400\ \Omega$ **20.** 60 Ω **21.** $I_1 = 90$ mA, $I_2 = 60$ mA, $R_T = 24\ \Omega$, $V_T = 3.6$ V **22.** $I_1 = 80$ mA, $I_2 = 40$ mA, $R_T = 60\ \Omega$, $V_T = 7.2$ V **23.** $I_1 = 150$ mA, $I_2 = 50$ mA, $R_T = 37.5\ \Omega$, $V_T = 7.5$ V **24.** $I_1 = 3.6$ mA, $I_2 = 24$ mA, $I_3 = 2.4$ mA, $R_T = 264\ \Omega$, $V_T = 7.92$ V **25.** $I_1 = 600$ mA, $I_2 = 200$ mA, $I_3 = 400$ mA, $R_T = 30\ \Omega$, $V_T = 36$ V **26.** $R_T = 30\ \Omega$, $V_T = 18$ V, $I_1 = 200$ mA, $I_2 = 200$ mA, $I_3 = 200$ mA **27.** $R_2 = 4\ \Omega$, $I_T = 6$ A, $I_1 = 1$ A, $I_2 = 3$ A, $I_3 = 2$ A **28.** $V_T = 24$ V, $I_T = 400$ mA, $I_1 = 133.33$ mA, $R_1 = 180\ \Omega$, $I_3 = 66.67$ mA **29.** $R_T = 7.5\ \Omega$, $V_T = 30$ V, $I_1 = 600$ mA, $I_2 = 100$ mA, $I_3 = 300$ mA, $I_4 = 3$ A **30.** $R_T = 100\ \Omega$, $I_T = 1.2$ A, $I_1 = 120$ mA, $I_2 = 80$ mA, $I_3 = 200$ mA, $I_4 = 800$ mA

JOBS 6-1 TO 6-3 **1.** $R_T = 6\ \Omega$, $I_T = 1.5$ A, $I_1 = 0.5$ A, $I_2 = I_3 = 1$ A, $V_1 = 9$ V, $V_2 = 6$ V, $V_3 = 3$ V **2.** $R_T = 44\ \Omega$, $I_T = 250$ mA, $I_1 = I_2 = 200$ mA, $I_3 = 50$ mA, $V_1 = 4.4$ V, $V_2 = 6.6$ V, $V_3 = 11$ V **3.** $R_T = 1.32$ kΩ, $I_T = 25$ mA, $I_1 = 10$ mA, $I_2 = I_3 = 15$ mA, $V_1 = 33$ V, $V_2 = 15$ V, $V_3 = 18$ V **4.** $R_T = 60\ \Omega$, $I_T = 2$ A, $I_1 = I_2 = 800$ mA, $I_3 = I_4 = 1.2$ A, $V_1 = 48$ V, $V_2 = 72$ V, $V_3 = 60$ V, $V_4 = 60$ V **5.** $R_T = 266.7\ \Omega$, $I_T = 225$ mA, $I_1 = I_2 = 150$ mA, $I_3 = I_4 = 75$ mA, $V_1 = 15$ V, $V_2 = 45$ V, $V_3 = 35.25$ V, $V_4 = 24.75$ V **6.** $R_T = 20\ \Omega$, $I_T = 1.8$ A, $I_1 = I_2 = 1.2$ A, $I_3 = I_4 = 400$ mA, $I_t = 200$ mA, $V_1 = 14.4$ V, $V_2 = 21.6$ V, $V_3 = 27.2$ V, $V_4 = 8.8$ V, $V_5 = 36$ V **7.** $R_T = 100\ \Omega$, $I_T = 240$ mA, $I_1 = I_2 = 120$ mA, $I_3 = I_4 = 40$ mA, $I_5 = I_6 = 80$ mA, $V_1 = 12$ V, $V_2 = 12$ V, $V_3 = 10.8$ V, $V_4 = 13.2$ V, $V_5 = 14.4$ V, $V_6 = 9.6$ V **8.** $R_T = 400\ \Omega$, $I_T = 40$ mA, $I_1 = 13.33$ mA, $I_2 = 6.67$ mA, $I_3 = 20$ mA, $I_4 = 26.67$ mA, $V_1 = 16$ V, $V_2 = 2.4$ V, $V_3 = 2.4$ V, $V_4 = 13.6$ V **9.** R_T increases and I_T decreases, but I_1 and I_2 remain the same. **10.** R_T decreases and I_T increases, but I_1, I_2, I_3, and I_4 remain the same. **11.** $R_T = 180\ \Omega$, $I_T = 200$ mA, $I_1 = 200$ mA, $I_2 = 120$ mA, $I_3 = 80$ mA, $V_1 = 24$ V, $V_2 = V_3 = 12$ V **12.** $R_T = 90\ \Omega$, $I_T = 100$ mA, $I_1 = 100$ mA, $I_2 = 40$ mA, $I_3 = 60$ mA, $V_1 = 1.8$ V, $V_2 = 7.2$ V, $V_3 = 7.2$ V **13.** $R_T = 60\ \Omega$, $I_T = 900$ mA, $I_1 = 900$ mA, $I_2 = 180$ mA, $I_3 = 720$ mA, $I_4 = 900$ mA, $V_1 = 27$ V, $V_2 = 18$ V, $V_3 = 18$ V, $V_4 = 9$ V **14.** $R_T = 300\ \Omega$, $I_T = 100$ mA, $I_1 = 100$ mA, $I_2 = 8$ mA, $I_3 = 80$ mA, $I_4 = 12$ mA, $V_1 = 3.6$ V, $V_2 = 26.4$ V, $V_3 = 26.4$ V, $V_4 = 26.4$ V **15.** $R_T = 50\ \Omega$, $I_T = 2$ A, $I_1 = 2$ A, $I_2 = 400$ mA, $I_3 = 400$ mA, $I_4 = 1.6$ A, $I_5 = 2$ A, $V_1 = 44$ V, $V_2 = 20$ V, $V_3 = 12$ V, $V_4 = 32$ V, $V_5 = 24$ V **16.** $R_T = 150\ \Omega$, $I_T = 160$ mA, $I_1 = 160$ mA, $I_2 = 120$ mA, $I_3 = 40$ mA, $I_4 = 40$ mA, $I_5 = 40$ mA, $I_6 = 160$ mA, $V_1 = 8$ V, $V_2 = 12$ V, $V_3 = 4$ V, $V_4 = 4$ V, $V_5 = 4$ V, $V_6 = 4$ V **17.** $R_T = 16\ \Omega$, $I_T = 2$ A, $I_1 = 2$ A,

$I_2 = 1$ A, $I_3 = 1$ A, $I_4 = 1$ A, $I_5 = 2$ A, $V_1 = 6$ V,
$V_2 = 6$ V, $V_3 = 12$ V, $V_4 = 18$ V, $V_5 = 8$ V
18. $R_T = 50$ Ω, $I_T = 480$ mA, $I_1 = 240$ mA, $I_2 = 240$ mA, $I_3 = 80$ mA, $I_4 = 160$ mA, $I_5 = 240$ mA,
$V_1 = 24$ V, $V_2 = 12$ V, $V_3 = 9.6$ V, $V_4 = 9.6$ V,
$V_5 = 2.4$ V   **19.** R_T and V_2 both increase.
20. R_T and V_4 both decrease.   **21.** $R_1 = 90$ Ω
22. $R_3 = 240$ Ω   **23.** $R_S = 115$ Ω   **24.** $R_2 = R_3 = 2$ kΩ   **25.** only the 12-V lamp

JOB 6-4   **1.** $V_{\text{line}} = 7.5$ V, $V_L = 112.5$ V   **2.** $V_{\text{line}} = 14.4$ V, $V_L = 105.6$ V   **3.** $V_G = 240$ V, $V_{\text{line}} = 7.5$ V
4. $V_{\text{line}} = 3.5$ V, $V_L = 236.5$ V   **5.** $V_L = 236$ V
6. $V_{\text{line}} = 1.5$ V   **7.** $R_1 = R_2 = 0.333$ Ω
8. $R_1 = R_2 = 1.25$ Ω   **9.** $I_3 = 1.5$ A   **10.** $I_1 = 4$ A
11. (a) $V_{\text{line}} = 5.6$ V, (b) $V_L = 109.4$ V
12. $V_L = 107$ V   **13.** 118.72 V   **14.** 1500 A. Yes, the fuse will blow instantly.   **15.** $V_G = 119$ V

JOBS 6-5 AND 6-6   **1.** (a) $V_{M_1} = 235.6$ V
(b) $V_{M_2} = 229.2$ V   (c) $V_{M_3} = 224.7$ V
2. (a) 117.6 V   (b) 115.5 V   **3.** (a) $V_B = 110$ V
(b) $V_G = 119$ V   **4.** (a) $V_A = 228.1$ V   (b) $I_C = 6$ A
(c) $V_G = 230$ V   **5.** (a) $V_A = 109$ V
(b) $V_B = 102.6$ V   **6.** (a) $V_A = 113.86$ V
(b) $V_B = 108.1$ V

JOBS 7-1 AND 7-2   **1.** $P = 1200$ W or 1.2 kW
2. $P = 0.54$ W or 540 mW   **3.** $P = 75$ W
4. $P = 30$ W   **5.** $P = 3.6$ W   **6.** $P = 69$ W
7. $P = 18$ W   **8.** (a) $P = 300$ W   (b) $P = 100$ W
9. $P = 1080$ W or 1.08 kW   **10.** $P = 25$ W
11. (a) 0.25 W or 250 mW   (b) 0.5 W or ½ W
12. (a) $P = 129.6$ mW   (b) $P = 86.4$ mW
13. $P = 3840$ W or 3.84 kW   **14.** $P = 1000$ W or 1 kW
15. $P = 0.5$ W or 500 mW   **16.** $P_T = 1800$ W
or 1.8 kW   **17.** $P_T = 30$ W   **18.** $P_T = 90$ W
19. $P_T = 2170$ W or 2.17 kW   **20.** $P_T = 62.1$ W
21. (a) $I_T = 300$ mA   (b) $P_1 = 900$ mW, $P_2 = 2.7$ W
(c) $P_T = 3.6$ W   **22.** (a) $I_T = 40$ mA
(b) $P_1 = 160$ mW, $P_2 = 240$ mW, $P_3 = 400$ mW
(c) $P_T = 800$ mW   **23.** (a) $P_1 = 108$ W, $P_2 = 72$ W
(b) $P_T = 180$ W   **24.** (a) $I_T = 1$ A   (b) $P_1 = 7.68$ W,
$P_2 = 11.52$ W, $P_3 = 3.2$ W, $P_4 = 1.6$ W   (c) $P_T = 24$ W
25. (a) $I_T = 120$ mA   (b) $P_1 = 1.44$ W, $P_2 = 5.184$ W,
$P_3 = 3.456$ W, $P_4 = 4.32$ W   (c) $P_T = 14.4$ W

JOB 7-3 AND 7-4   **1.** $I = 2.5$ A   **2.** $I = 8.75$ A
3. $I = 12.5$ A   **4.** $V = 50$ V   **5.** $V = 40$ V
6. $I = 5$ A   **8.** $V = 10.8$ V   **9.** (a) $I = 625$ mA
(b) $I_T = 3.75$ A   **10.** (a) $I = 2.083$ A
(b) $I = 416.67$ mA   (c) $I = 833.3$ mA
(d) $I_T = 3.33$ A   **11.** yes   **12.** $P = 1.28$ W

13. $P = 6$ mW   **14.** $P = 40$ mW   **15.** $P = 25$ W
16. $R_T = 160$ Ω, $I_T = 200$ mA, $V_1 = 8$ V, $V_2 = 24$ V,
$P_1 = 1.6$ W, $P_2 = 4.8$ W, $P_T = 6.4$ W   **17.** $I_1 = 100$ mA,
$I_2 = 50$ mA, $I_T = 150$ mA, $R_T = 66.67$ Ω, $P_1 = 1$ W,
$P_2 = 0.5$ W or 500 mW, $P_T = 1.5$ W   **18.** $I_T = 500$ mA,
$V_T = 50$ V, $R_2 = 10$ Ω, $V_1 = 7.5$ V, $V_3 = 15$ V,
$V_4 = 22.5$ V, $P_1 = 3.75$ W, $P_3 = 7.5$ W, $P_4 = 11.25$ W,
$P_T = 25$ W   **19.** $I_T = 8$ A, $R_T = 15$ Ω, $R_3 = 120$ Ω,
$I_1 = 3$ A, $I_2 = 4$ A, $I_3 = 1$ A, $P_1 = 360$ W, $P_2 = 480$ W,
$P_3 = 120$ W   **20.** $R_T = 1.2$ kΩ, $I_T = 30$ mA,
$P_1 = 198$ mW, $P_2 = 67.5$ mW, $P_3 = 612$ mW,
$P_4 = 50.625$ mW, $P_5 = 60.75$ mW, $P_6 = 91.125$ mW,
$P_T = 1.08$ W

JOBS 7-5 AND 7-6   **1.** 10^4 **2.** 10^8 **3.** 10^3 **4.** 10^{15}
5. 10^{-6} **6.** 10^{-20} **7.** 10^9 **8.** 10^{-24} **9.** 4×10^6
10. 2.56×10^4 **11.** 56.25×10^{-6} **12.** 9×10^{-6}
13. 2.56×10^{-4} **14.** 16×10^8 **15.** 1×10^{-8}
16. 4×10^6 **17.** 1   **18.** 9×10^8 **19.** 81×10^8
20. 36×10^{-10} **21.** $P = 40$ mW   **22.** $P = 90$ mW
23. $P = 200$ W   **24.** (a) $P = 50$ W (b) $P = 200$ W
25. $P = 100$ W   **26.** (a) $P = 1$ W, (b) 2 W
27. $P = 360$ W   **28.** $P = 600$ W
29. $P = 112.5$ W   **30.** $P = 1.88$ W
31. (a) $P_1 = 4.5$ W   (b) $P_2 = 2.7$ W
(c) $P_T = 7.2$ W   **32.** (a) $P_1 = 4.5$ W
(b) $P_2 = 7.5$ W   (c) $P_T = 12$ W

JOBS 7-7 TO 7-9   **1.** 44   **2.** 22   **3.** 11   **4.** 27.5
5. 17.4   **6.** 165   **7.** 6.7   **8.** 3.3   **9.** 14.8   **10.** 25.5
11. 10^4 **12.** 10^{-4} **13.** 8×10^2 **14.** 6×10^2
15. 9×10^{-2} **16.** 10×10^{-2} **17.** 2×10^2
18. 1.1×10^2 **19.** 1.34×10^4 **20.** 2.5×10^{-5}

JOBS 7-10 AND 7-11   **1.** $I = 100$ mA
2. $I = 14.14$ mA   **3.** $V = 120$ V   **4.** $V = 111.8$ V
5. $I = 22.36$ mA   **6.** $V = 20.98$ V   **7.** $I = 10$ A
8. $V = 12.65$ V   **9.** $I = 1.414$ A   **10.** $R = 192$ Ω
11. $P_1 = 125$ mW, $P_2 = 250$ mW, $P_3 = 375$ mW,
$P_T = 750$ mW   **12.** $P_1 = 900$ mW, $P_2 = 600$ mW,
$P_3 = 750$ mW, $P_T = 2.25$ W   **13.** $V_T = 12$ V,
$I_1 = 400$ mA, $I_2 = 600$ mA, $I_3 = 200$ mA, $I_T = 1.2$ A,
$P_1 = 4.8$ W, $P_3 = 2.4$ W, $P_T = 14.4$ W

JOBS 8-1 AND 8-2   **1.** $14b$ **2.** $18x$ **3.** $18y$
4. $13.5p$ **5.** $8.5c$ **6.** $20I$ **7.** $20a$ **8.** $64W$
9. 6μ **10.** $14X$ **11.** 15 mA   **12.** $7I_2$ **13.** $7a$
14. $8a$ **15.** $68c$ **16.** $18x + 11y$ **17.** $6I + 3X$
18. $19W + 7X$ **19.** $15a + 2p$ **20.** $7 + 27R$
21. $22w + 30x - 6c$ **22.** $3p - 3b$ **23.** a
24. $7 + 5I$ **25.** $6a + 10x$ **26.** $19p - 18a$
27. $3.5x - 0.5a$ **28.** $20x - 7w$ **29.** $4 - a$

30. $150 - 55I$ **31.** $R_T = 6R_1$ **32.** $R_T = 8R_2$
33. $I_T = 10I_1$ **34.** $I_1 = 3I_2$ **35.** $R_2 = 2R_1$

JOB 8-3 **1.** $X = 5$ **2.** $R = 7$ **3.** $X = 8$ **4.** $a = 4$
5. $P = 90$ **6.** $X = 8$ **7.** $a = 112$ **8.** $b = 8.67$
9. $I = 3$ **10.** $X = 120$ **11.** $a = 10$ **12.** $X = 19.2$
13. $R = 5$ **14.** $X = 19$ **15.** $X = 9$ **16.** $R = 8$
17. $X = 150$ **18.** $a = 9$ **19.** $b = 24$ **20.** $L = 7$
21. $X = 3$ **22.** $Q = 3$ **23.** $X = 110$ **24.** $M = 10$
25. $X = 20$ **26.** $R_1 = 200 \ \Omega, R_2 = 600 \ \Omega$
27. (a) $2R + 1000 \ \Omega = 2400 \ \Omega$ (b) $R = 700 \ \Omega$
28. $\beta = 100$ **29.** $I_2 = 2 \ \text{A}$ **30.** $I_A = 2.4 \ \text{A}$,
$I_B = 7.2 \ \text{A}, I_C = 14.4 \ \text{A}$

JOBS 8-4 AND 8-5 **1.** $x = 8$ **2.** $Q = 260$ **3.** $y = 8$
4. $A = 252$ **5.** $x = 108$ **6.** $F = 60$ **7.** $x = 64$
8. $x = 441$ **9.** $x = 344$ **10.** $C = 9$ **11.** $x = 52$
12. $x = 15$ **13.** $Q = 306$ **14.** $x = 90$ **15.** $x = 21$
16. $5a + 11$ **17.** $14x + 3$ **18.** $-9 - 6p$
19. $1 + 2y$ **20.** $32 - 19b$ **21.** $19 + 5x$
22. 3 **23.** $-20 - 3Z$ **24.** $3 - a + b$ **25.** $5 + 5x$
26. radio $= 0.375 \ \text{A}$, light $= 1.125 \ \text{A}$ **27.** TV $= 3 \ \text{A}$,
VCR $= 2 \ \text{A}$, lamp $= 0.8 \ \text{A}$

JOBS 8-6 AND 8-7 **1.** $x = 1$ **2.** $a = 3$ **3.** $y = 4$
4. $I = 6$ **5.** $T = 0.5$ **6.** $x = 2$ **7.** $I = \frac{1}{3}$
8. $R = \frac{1}{3}$ **9.** $x = 9$ **10.** $b = 6$ **11.** $x = 16$
12. $x = 2$ **13.** $y = 2.1$ **14.** $x = 2.5$ **15.** $x = 20$
16. $y = -9$ **17.** $x = -3$ **18.** $x = -3$ **19.** $x = -4$
20. $R = 3$ **21.** $x = -1$ **22.** $x = -13$ **23.** $P = -3$
24. $R = -7$ **25.** $x = -60$

JOBS 8-8 TO 8-10 **1.** $30 + 10a$ **2.** $8x + 32$
3. $6x - 30$ **4.** $22 - 12x$ **5.** $5Q + 1$ **6.** $30 + 3I_3$
7. $7x - 16$ **8.** $4I_1 - 10$ **9.** $2y + 6$ **10.** $6 - 4x$
11. $x = 2$ **12.** $x = 11$ **13.** $Z = 1$ **14.** $x = 6$
15. $x = -4$ **16.** $a = 6$ **17.** $x = 0$ **18.** $I_2 = 5$
19. $F = -9$ **20.** $V = 13$ **21.** $x = 12$ **22.** $V = 90$
23. $x = 40$ **24.** $y = 36$ **25.** $a = 24$ **26.** $I_B = 80 \ \mu\text{A}$
27. $R_E = 145 \ \Omega$ **28.** $r_e' = 20 \ \Omega$

JOBS 8-11 TO 8-13 **1.** $x = 6, y = 2$ **2.** $x = 5, y = 3$
3. $V = \frac{178}{33}, I = -\frac{240}{33}$ **4.** $a = 2.5, b = 4$ **5.** $Z = 2$,
$R = 3$ **6.** $R_1 = 1, R_2 = 3$ **7.** $S = -2, x = 2$
8. $x = -5, y = 3$ **9.** $x = 1, y = 1$ **10.** $x = 0, y = 18$
11. $x = 0, y = 1$ **12.** $x = 8, y = 1$

JOBS 9-1 TO 9-4 **1.** $13 \ \text{A}$ **2.** $I = 2 \ \text{A}, V_1 = 4 \ \text{V}$,
$V_2 = 8 \ \text{V}, V_3 = 12 \ \text{V}$ **3.** $I = 1 \ \text{A}$ **4.** $R_2 = 6.2 \ \Omega$
5. $V_G = 480 \ \text{V}, I_1 = 6 \ \text{A}, I_2 = 8 \ \text{A}$ **6.** V_T, V_1, V_2,
$V_3 = 140 \ \text{V}, I_3 = 7.15 \ \text{A}, R_3 = 19.58 \ \Omega, R_T = 9.66 \ \Omega$
7. $R_3 = 22 \ \Omega$ **8.** $I_4 = 2 \ \text{A}; V_2 = V_3 = V_4 = 72 \ \text{V}$,
$R_2 = 18 \ \Omega, R_3 = 12 \ \Omega, V_1 = 168 \ \text{V}, R_T = 20 \ \Omega$

JOBS 9-5 AND 9-6 **1.** $I_1 = 3.09 \ \text{A}, I_2 = 0.36 \ \text{A}$,
$I_L = 3.45 \ \text{A}$ **2.** $I_1 = 5.18 \ \text{A}, I_2 = 7.98 \ \text{A}, I_3 = 2.8 \ \text{A}$
3. $I = 2.04 \ \text{A}$ **4.** $R_x = 2 \ \Omega$

JOB 9-7 **1.** $R_a = 2.65 \ \Omega, R_b = 1.59 \ \Omega, R_c = 0.88 \ \Omega$
2. $A = 7.5, B = 12.25, C = 4.69$

JOBS 9-8 AND 9-9 **1.** $I_L = 1.92 \ \text{A}, P_L = 276.5 \ \text{W}$
2. $I_L = 0.196 \ \text{A}$

JOBS 10-1 AND 10-2 **1.** $R_{SH} = 11.1 \ \Omega$
2. $I_T = 0.26 \ \text{A}$ **3.** $R_M = 4.5 \ \Omega$ **4.** $R_{SH} = 0.612 \ \Omega$

JOBS 10-3 AND 10-4 **1.** $1400 \ \Omega$ **2.** $R_{mult} = 9500 \ \Omega$
3. $R_{mult} = 999,500 \ \Omega$ **4.** $I = 50 \ \text{mA}$ **5.** $V_T = 10 \ \text{V}$
6. $R_{mult} = 3600 \ \Omega$ **7.** (a) $I_m = 0.1$
(b) $R_{mult} = 900 \ \Omega$

JOB 10-5 **1.** $V_1 = 18.75 \ \text{V}, V_2 = 7.5 \ \text{V}, V_3 = 3.75 \ \text{V}$
2. $R_2 = 13.34 \ \Omega$ **3.** $R_1 = 847 \ \Omega, R_2 = 3448 \ \Omega$,
$R_3 = 11,111 \ \Omega$ **4.** $R_1 = 1389 \ \Omega, R_2 = 3906 \ \Omega$,
$R_3 = 8333 \ \Omega, R_4 = 379 \ \Omega$

JOBS 10-6 TO 10-8 **1.** $R_a = 6000 \ \Omega$ **2.** $V_2 = 7.49 \ \text{V}$
3. $R_x = 5000 \ \Omega$ **4.** (a) $V_{TH} = 2.13 \ \text{V}$
(b) $R_{TH} = 1499 \ \Omega$ (c) $I_L = 1 \ \text{mA}$ **5.** $I_L = 11.9 \ \text{mA}$

JOBS 10-9 AND 10-10 **1.** $I_{RL} = 6.96 \ \text{mA}$,
$V_{RL} = 6.96 \ \text{V}, V_C = -2.04 \ \text{V}$ **2.** $I_C = 1.44 \ \text{mA}$,
$I_E = 1.47 \ \text{mA}, V_C = 10.58 \ \text{V}, V_{RL} = 1.42 \ \text{V}$

JOB 10-11 **1.** (a) $V_{CE} = 4 \ \text{V}$ (b) $I_b = 4.4 \ \text{mA}$
(c) $I_c = 1.004 \ \text{mA}$

JOB 10-12 **1.** $R_1 = 24 \ \Omega, R_2 = 7.46 \ \Omega$
2. $R_1 = 38.7 \ \Omega, R_2 = 290 \ \Omega, R_3 = 38.7 \ \Omega$

JOB 10-13 **1.** $P_L = 0.00055 \ \text{W}, P_3 = 0.00035 \ \text{W}$
2. $P_L = 1.42 \ \text{W}, P_2 = 2.83 \ \text{W}$ **3.** $P_L = 0.05 \ \text{W}$
4. $P_1 = 720 \ \text{W}, P_2 = 240 \ \text{W}$ **5.** $P_1 = 40 \ \text{W}$,
$P_2 = 200 \ \text{W}, P_3 = 200 \ \text{W}$

JOBS 11-1 TO 11-3 **1.** 82% **2.** 32.64% **3.** 0.7%
4. 153.5% **5.** 3.14% **6.** 67.16% **7.** 3162.5%
8. 379.67% **9.** 32.39% **10.** 21.9% **11.** 0.0122
12. 0.135 **13.** 2.052 **14.** 0.618 **15.** 3.73
16. 0.000081 **17.** 0.0051 **18.** 1.435 **19.** 0.0704
20. 0.00003 **21.** 0.00025 **22.** 0.1508 **23.** 5502%
24. 50% **25.** 107% **26.** 3,850% **27.** 27%
28. 1153% **29.** 0.79% **30.** 3.7% **31.** 241%
32. 10,370% **33.** 532.7% **34.** 20,130% **35.** 252.9%
36. 16.67% **37.** 72.72% **38.** 5.35% **39.** 12.5%
40. 266.67% **41.** 0.52% **42.** 90% **43.** 43.3%
44. 1.94% **45.** 0.8 **46.** 1.2 **47.** 3.4 **48.** 0.567
49. 0.001 **50.** 7.205 **51.** 0.027 **52.** 0.428
53. 0.0003 **54.** 0.0063 **55.** 197.08 **56.** 77.86

57. 816.25 **58.** 0.254 **59.** 515.75 **60.** 3.94
61. 0.2 **62.** 38.4 **63.** 176.25 **64.** 4.15 **65.** 150
66. 32.73 **67.** 300 **68.** 440 **69.** 54 **70.** 290
71. 109.6 **72.** 264 **73.** 62.78 **74.** 940
75. min: 1425 Ω, max: 1575 Ω **76.** (a) + or −230 Ω
(b) + or −300,000 Ω (c) + or −47,200 Ω
(d) + or −225,000 Ω (e) + or − 53,630 Ω
(f) + or −0.037 Ω (g) + or −5.42 Ω
(h) + or −0.057 Ω (i) + or −150 Ω
(j) + or −1185 Ω **77.** 93.3 V
78. (a) min: 308.75 V, max: 341.25 V
(b) min: 451.25 V, max: 498.75 V
(c) min: 34.68 V, max: 38.33 V
(d) min: 1.97 V, max: 2.17 V **79.** $415.75
80. (a) $178 ($b$) 10.38% **81.** $471.42
82. tax: $37.71, cost: $509.13 **83.** 41.48%
84. 42.4% **85.** min: 87.23 MHz, max: 88.37 MHz
86. 23 A **87.** 50 resistors: 46.3%, 27 capacitors: 25%,
14 transistors: 12.96%, 17 ICs: 15.74%
88. no (108 V is minimum voltage) **89.** $661.25
90. voltage drop in line: 6.6 V, voltage supplied to
load: 213.4 V **91.** 14% **92.** 123.08 V
93. 3244.8 rpm **94.** 1184.23 Hz **95.** No. 22 wire:
9.08 kg, No. 18 wire: 6.57 kg, No. 24 wire: 21.15 kg,
No. 14 wire: 16.6 kg **96.** (a) 21.21 V (b) 19.08 V
(c) 60 V

JOB 11-4 **1.** 5300 W **2.** 2238 W **3.** 3.2 kW
4. 1.492 kW **5.** 93.25 W **6.** 6.7 hp **7.** 8952 W
8. 39,830 W **9.** 36.73 hp **10.** 1119 kW **11.** 0.6 hp
12. 90.48 hp **13.** 4,252.2 W **14.** 3.69 hp
15. 18.65 hp **16.** 1,081.7 kW **17.** 9.17 hp
18. 7,833 W **19.** 1.68 hp **20.** 5,147.4 W

JOBS 11-5 AND 11-6 **1.** 96.9% **2.** 4.15 hp
3. (a) 4,899 W (b) 83.8% **4.** 92% **5.** 89.5%
6. 83.1% **7.** 92% **8.** 89% **9.** 95.6% **10.** 78%
11. 62% **12.** 89.5% **13.** 86.7% **14.** 67%
15. 61.5% **16.** 9.215 kW **17.** 16.4 hp
18. 16.96 hp **19.** 10.17 A **20.** 8.338 kW **21.** 85.3%
22. 1.1 hp **23.** 10.289 kW **24.** 17.1 hp
25. 11.19 kW **26.** 19.6 hp **27.** 91.687 kW
28. 7.3 hp **29.** 88.2 W **30.** (a) 6527.5 W
(b) 28.4 A **31.** (a) 3 Ω (b) 468.8 W **32.** 1521 W

JOBS 12-1 TO 12-3 **1.** 3:4 **2.** 5:3 **3.** 5:1 **4.** 9:1:3
5. 2:3:4 **6.** 2:3 **7.** 11:12 **8.** 4:9 **9.** 3:4 **10.** 7:9
11. 11:12 **12.** 3:4 **13.** 36/60 **14.** 16/60 **15.** 35/60
16. 34, 51, 68 **17.** 10, 6 **18.** 9:1 **19.** 5:1
20. 625.2 ft **21.** $33.45 **22.** $R = 4.394\ \Omega$
23. 1:1.34 **24.** eff = 84.8% **25.** $\beta = 50$
26. PF = 16.7% **27.** $Q = 44$ **28.** $R_x = 148.8\ \Omega$

29. $V_x = 58.7$ V **30.** (a) 28 (b) $\frac{1}{9}$ **31.** 54 kg of
sand, 32.4 kg of gravel, 21.6 kg of cement
32. $R = 25.8\ \Omega$ **33.** 18.24 ft **34.** 114 kg copper,
66 kg zinc **35.** $I_2 = 25$ A **36.** $R_2 = 17.45\ \Omega$
37. 1083.3 rpm

JOB 12-4 **1.** 30; 0.01003; 100.5 **2.** 90.74; 0.0907;
8234 **3.** 25; 17.90; 0.0179 **4.** 0; 324.9; 105,500
5. 57.07; 0.0571; 3257 **6.** 17; 45.26; 2048
7. 460.0; 0.460; 211,600 **8.** 00; 364.8; 0.3648
9. 35; 0.005615; 31.52 **10.** 1; 289.3; 0.2893

JOBS 12-5 TO 12-10 **1.** $R_I = 6.5\ \Omega$
2. $R_S = 18.23\ \Omega$ **3.** No. 11 AWG **4.** $R = 899.4\ \Omega$
5. (a) $R = 131.25\ \Omega$ (b) $I = 0.88$ A
(c) $P = 100.8$ W **6.** $L = 1000$ ft. **7.** $I = 841.15$ ft
8. $L = 150.9$ ft **9.** No. 18 AWG **10.** $D = 16.18$ mil

JOB 12-11 **1.** $R = 55.6\ \Omega$ **2.** $R = 55.4\ \Omega$
3. $T_2 = 180.7°C$

JOB 13-1 **1.** 0.1966 Ω **2.** 1.392 Ω **3.** No. 12 wire
4. No. 0 wire **5.** $R = 0.02146\ \Omega$ **6.** $R = 0.309\ \Omega$
7. $L = 3640$ ft **8.** $R = 1.23\ \Omega$ **9.** $R = 0.635\ \Omega$
10. $R = 2.34\ \Omega$ **11.** $I = 635.9$ ft **12.** $I = 3144.68$ ft
13. 55 A **14.** 39.96 V **15.** No. 3 AWG
16. $R = 0.000249\ \Omega/\text{ft}$ **17.** $L = 498$ ft

JOB 13-2 **1.** No. 12 **2.** No. 8 **3.** No. 6
4. No. 8 **5.** No. 4 **6.** No. 10 **7.** No. 10
8. No. 00 **9.** (a) 1253 W (b) No. 4 **10.** No. 4

JOB 13-3 AND 13-4 **1.** No. 00 **2.** (a) $V_d = 12$ V
(b) $V_L = 108$ V **3.** $V_d = 47$ V **4.** No. 000
5. No. 3 **6.** No. 6 **7.** No. 8 **8.** No. 4 **9.** No. 2
10. $L = 345.9$ ft

JOBS 14-1 AND 14-2 **1.** sin $\angle X = 0.667$,
cos $\angle X = 0.5$, tan $\angle X = 1.333$ **2.** sin $\angle D = 0.923$,
cos $\angle D = 0.385$, tan $\angle D = 2.4$ **3.** (a) sin $\angle A = 0.5$,
cos $\angle A = 0.7$, tan $\angle A = 0.714$ (b) sin $\angle D = 0.923$,
cos $\angle D = 0.417$, tan $\angle D = 2.4$ (c) sin $\angle J = 0.778$,
cos $\angle J = 0.444$, tan $\angle J = 1.75$ (d) sin $\angle M = 0.333$,
cos $\angle M = 0.833$, tan $\angle M = 0.4$ (e) sin $\angle P = 0.385$,
cos $\angle P = 0.923$, tan $\angle P = 0.417$ (f) sin $\angle Z = 0.733$,
cos $\angle Z = 0.8$, tan $\angle Z = 0.917$ **4.** 0.2924 **5.** 0.6820
6. 11.430 **7.** 0.8910 **8.** 0.6249 **9.** 0.9511
10. 0.6018 **11.** 0.3256 **12.** 0.0699 **13.** 51°
14. 6° **15.** 87° **16.** 7° **17.** 55° **18.** 15° **19.** 77°
20. 41° **21.** 48° **22.** 26° **23.** 85° **24.** 10°
25. 60° **26.** 11° **27.** 84° **28.** 81° **29.** 52°
30. 47°

JOB 14-3 **1.** $\angle A = 58°$, $\angle B = 32°$ **2.** $\angle A = 54°$,
$\angle B = 36°$ **3.** $\angle A = 42°$, $\angle B = 48°$ **4.** $\angle A = 70°$,

$\angle B = 20°$ **5.** $\angle A = 23°$, $\angle B = 67°$ **6.** $\angle A = 65°$, $\angle B = 25°$ **7.** 26° **8.** 961.4 ft **9.** 29,621.97 m **10.** $V_T = 80.6$ V, $V_L = 58.9$ V **11.** $A = 41°$ **12.** 34° **13.** 157.9 VA

JOBS 14-4 AND 14-5 **1.** $AC = 9.89$ m, $\angle B = 18°$ **2.** $BC = 24.09$ in, $\angle B = 55°$ **3.** $AC = 82$ cm, $\angle A = 45°$ **4.** $AC = 303$ V, $\angle B = 60°$ **5.** $AB = 181$ W, $\angle B = 62°$ **6.** $BC = 642.7$ ft, $\angle A = 55°$ **7.** $AC = 32.45$ in., $\angle A = 72°$ **8.** $BC = 150.4$ V, $\angle B = 67°$ **9.** $BC = 30.1$ in., $\angle B = 48°$ **10.** (*a*) $\theta = 25°$ (*b*) $V_T = 193.7$ V **11.** (*a*) $V_L = 19,156$ Ω (*b*) 26° **12.** 26° **13.** $AB = 4.59$ in. **14.** 8.66 in. **15.** 62° **16.** 933 ft **17.** 34° **18.** 41 cm

JOB 15-1
1. See Fig. 6.

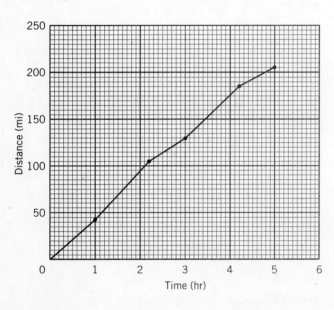

2. See Fig. 7.

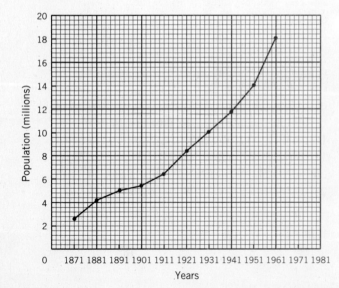

3. See Fig. 8.

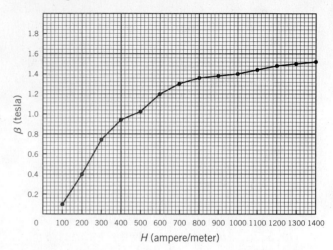

4. See Fig. 9.

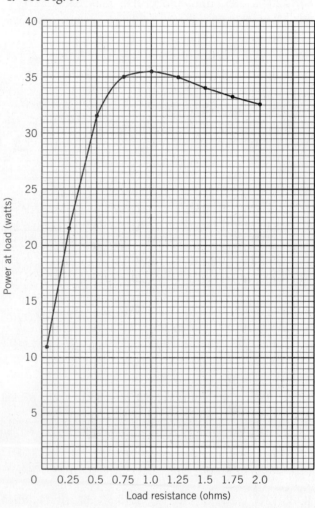

5. See Fig. 10.

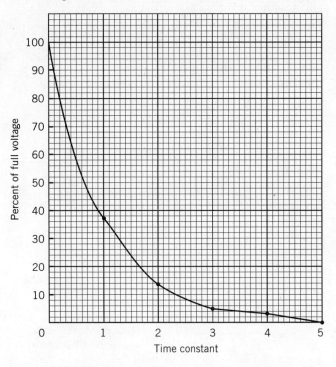

JOBS 15-2 TO 15-4   **1.** 491.8 m   **2.** 3.38 m
3. 3.1,621,621 Hz   **4.** 109.1 V   **5.** 115.34 mA
6. 152.47 V   **7.** 28°   **8.** 148.5 V   **9.** 5.66 A
10. 113.12 V, 5.66 A

JOBS 15-5 AND 15-6   **1.** (a) 8.9 MHz   (b) 52 kHz
(c) 98 Hz   **2.** 142.8 μs   **3.** 210 V   **4.** (a) 2.8 V
(b) 0.19 Hz   **5.** 1:7 volts per division   **6.** 52×10^{-4}
seconds per division   **7.** $I = 1.6$ A   **8.** $V = 104.3$ V,
$R = 9.07$ Ω **9.** $V = 335.4$ V   **10.** $I = 1.85$ A

JOB 15-7   **1.** 6.0   **2.** 10.7   **3.** 14.1   **4.** 90.98
5. 26.6 cm   **6.** 127.3 ft   **7.** 27.75 ft
8. $XY = 12.5$ ft, $YZ = 4.93$ ft, $ZW = 26.8$ ft

JOB 15-8   **1.** 0.02 A   **2.** 192.3 V   **3.** 67.3 W
4. $X_L = 1760$ Ω, $L = 0.56$ H   **5.** PF = 0.11
6. $I = 0.024$ A   **7.** 2.46 W   **8.** 84°

JOB 15-9   **1.** fundamental frequency plus its harmonics   **2.** Any signal voltage can be represented as
the sum of harmonics. Network components such as
filters and audio amplifiers function in terms of frequency response to each of the harmonics.   In non-
linear components such as power supplies that use
diodes, it can produce pulses of currents in branch
circuits. The current pulses are full of harmonics that
cause interference with devices such as a TV set. It can
also produce false digital signals that can confuse a
digital system operating in the same component.

JOB 16-1   **1.** Magnetomotive force (mmf) is the
force that establishes magnetic lines of force. It is

directly created by the electric current flow in a wire
or coil. The magnitude of the flux is directly propor-
tional to the number of turns in the coil and the magnitude of the current.   **2.** Reluctance (R) of a magnetic circuit is similar to electric circuit resistance. It
can be defined as the constant proportionality
between the mmf and the magnetic flux (ϕ).
3. Permeability (μ) is the ability of a material to
permit the establishment of flux.   **4.** Flux density
(β) is defined as the flux per unit of cross-sectional
area.   **5.** Magnetizing force (H) or magnetic intensi-
ty is the amount of mmf per unit length of a magnetic circuit.   **6.** The amount of flux is dependent on
the number of turns in the coil and the current flow
through the coil. However, increasing the length of
the magnetic circuit increases the difficulty of flux
development.

JOB 16-2   **1.** Inductance is the ability of a conductor
to produce induced voltage within itself or another
conductor when the current varies.   **2.** The amount
of inductive reactance in a coil depends on the
amount of inductance and the frequency of the alter-
nating current.   **3.** (a) 942,000 Ω (b) 14,130,000 Ω
4. 48 mH   **5.** 2200 Ω **6.** 955 Hz   **7.** (a) 157 Ω
(b) 0.7 A   **8.** 3317 mH   **9.** (a) 4789 Ω
(b) 0.037 A

JOBS 16-3 TO 16-6   **1.** (a) 1184 Ω (b) 1910 Ω
(c) 0.058 A   (d) $V_R = 86.4$ V, $V_L = 68.7$ V
(e) 38° lag   (f) 78.8%   (g) 5.04 W   **2.** (a) 2638 Ω
(b) 2898 Ω (c) 0.058 A   (d) 153 V   (e) 168 V
(f) 65°   (g) 42.3% lag   (h) 4.02 W   **3.** 767 Ω
4. (a) 2.43   (b) 18.4 Ω **5.** 70   **6.** 6.5 H
7. 1.09 H   **8.** 0.28 H   **9.** 1.9 H

JOBS 16-7 TO 16-10   **1.** 6.59×10^{-3} Ω
2. (a) $L = 0.0394$ mH   (b) $X_L = 0.0149$ Ω
(c) 46 V   (d) 0.304   **3.** 1569   **4.** 50.3 V
5. 1530   **6.** 9.58   **7.** 11:1   **8.** $N_p = 550$, 230 extra
turns   **9.** 150 A   **10.** 1.64 A   **11.** (a) 1.8 A
(b) 13.9 A   (c) 16.2 W   **12.** 0.61 A   **13.** (a) 22 V
(b) 4.9 A   (c) 107.6 W   **14.** 1.7:1   **15.** 60,750 Ω
16. 17.8%

JOBS 16-12 AND 16-13   **1.** (a) 330 W   (b) 228 W
(c) 69%   **2.** (a) 60%   (b) 1 A   **3.** (a) 637 W
(b) 25.5 A   **4.** (a) 36.7 W   (b) 44.5 V
5. (a) $P_p = 60.75$ W   (b) $V_p = 81$ V

JOB 16-14   **1.** No. 14: 1285, No. 12: 1286, No. 10:
1277, No. 8: 1304

JOBS 17-1 TO 17-6   **1.** A capacitor passes alternat-
ing current and blocks direct current.   **2.** Area of the

plates, distance between the plates, insulating or dielectric material   **3.** Working voltage is the maximum voltage that can be applied to a capacitor without destroying it.   **4.** $C_T = 90\ \mu F$ **5.** 0.02915 μF, 50 V   **6.** 0.000 072 097 F   **7.** 9.23 μF   **8.** 165 μF, 220 V   **9.** 0.0188 μF   **10.** 10 μF   **11.** (a) 225.8 Ω   (b) 30.9 Ω   (c) 3.39 Ω   **12.** (a) 7,582.6 Ω   (b) 5,896,226 Ω   **13.** (a) 663 Ω   (b) 0.18 A   **14.** (a) 331.7 Ω   (b) 0.36 A   **15.** 20 μF   **16.** 13,816 Hz   **17.** 240 μF   **18.** (a) 0.08 V   (b) 0 W

JOB 17-7   **1.** (a) 1327 Ω   (b) 0.12 A   (c) 917 Ω   (d) 42°   (e) 75% leading   (f) 9.8 W   **2.** (a) 85.7% of the 1-kHz audio frequency passes through the resistor.   (b) 0.016% of the 10-MHz radio frequency passes through the resistor.   **3.** (a) 118 Ω   (b) 0.36   (c) 0.92 A   (d) 0.99 A   (e) 1.09 Ω   (f) 69°   (g) 35.8% leading   (h) 38.9 W   **4.** (a) 427 Ω   (b) 0.15 A   (c) 0.5 A   (d) 0.52 A   (e) 423 Ω   (f) 73°   (g) 29.24% leading   (h) 33.7 W

JOBS 18-2 AND 18-3   **1.** (a) 2035 Ω   (b) 90 V   (c) 150 V   (d) 175 V   (e) 59° lagging   **2.** (a) 0.14 A   (b) 91 V   (c) 52° lagging   (d) 4.08 μF   (e) 821 Ω   **3.** (a) 41 Ω   (b) 204 Ω   (c) 0.8A   (d) 160 V   (e) 32.8 V   (f) 12°   (g) 97.8% lagging   (h) 129 W   **4.** 68.12 Hz   **5.** 478 Ω   **6.** (a) 212 Ω   (b) 659 Ω   (c) 471 Ω   (d) 0.025 A   (e) 5.3 V   (f) 16.5 V   (g) 3.75 V   (h) 71°   (i) 32.56% leading   (j) 0.96 W   **7.** (a) 160 Ω   (b) 221 Ω   (c) 0.2   (d) 306 Ω   (d) 306 Ω   (e) 0.28 A   (f) 62 V   **8.** (a) 0.7 A   (b) 171 Ω   (c) 161 Ω   (d) 44.9 μF

JOBS 18-4 AND 18-5   **1.** (a) 1213 Hz   (b) 571 Ω   (c) 571 Ω   (d) 21 Ω   (e) 0.048 A   (f) 27.2 V   **2.** 93.9 μF   **3.** 3533.3 Hz   **4.** 284 μH   **5.** (a) 9012 Ω   (b) 42.8 μF   (c) 45 Ω

JOBS 19-1 TO 19-4   **1.** (a) 15.8 Ω   (b) 7.3 A   (c) 100%   (d) 841.9 W   **2.** (a) 0.05 A, 0.03 A   (b) 0.08 A   (c) 1375 Ω   (d) 0   (e) 0 W   **3.** (a) 1.27 A, 2.06 A   (b) 3.33 A   (c) 31.5 Ω   (d) 0   (e) 0 W   **4.** (a) 1: at 1 kHz, $I_L = 0.069\ A$, $I_R = 0.019\ A$, 2: at 1 MHz, $I_L = 0.000069\ A$, $I_R = 0.019\ A$ (b) 1: at 1 KHz, $I_T = 0.07\ A$, 2: at 1 MHz, $I_T = 0.0189\ A$ (c) 1: at 1 KHz, percent of total current passing through R is 27%, 2: at 1 MHz, percent of total current passing through R is 100%   **5.** (a) $I_R = 3.29\ A$, $I_L = 2.56\ A$, $I_C = 4.79\ A$ (b) 3.97 A   (c) 34°   (d) 28.9 Ω   (e) 82.9% leading   (f) 378.6 W

6. $R = 24\ \Omega$, $X_L = 16\ \Omega$, $L = 42\ mH$ **7.** (a) 3.66 A   (b) 1.83 A   (c) 1.37 A   (d) 3.68 A   (e) 7°   (f) 29.9 Ω   (g) 99.3% lagging   (h) 402 W   **8.** $I_R = 6.45\ A$, $I_{react} = 11.17\ A$ **9.** $I_R = 3.59\ A$, $I_{react} = 2.71\ A$

JOB 19-6
1. See Fig. 11.

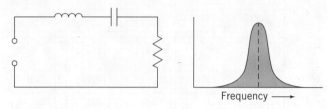

2. See Fig. 12.

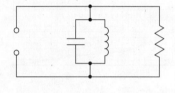 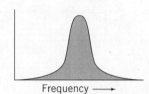

3. See Fig. 13.

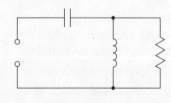 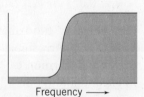

4. See Fig. 14.

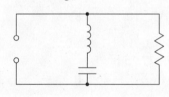 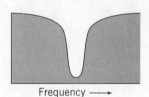

5. See Fig. 15.

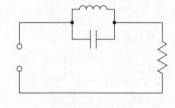 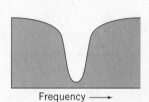

6. See Fig. 16.

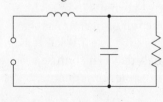 

7. (*a*) 17.3 A   (*b*) 13.87 Ω   (*c*) 4.7°   (*d*) 99.6% lagging   (*e*) 4130 W   **8.** (*a*) 16.97 A   (*b*) 14.14 Ω   (*c*) 3934.08 W   (*d*) 14.9°   (*e*) 96.6% lagging

JOB 19-7   **1.** (*a*) $Z_{eq} = 25$ Ω   (*b*) $I_T = 9.6$ A   (*c*) θ = 33% leading   (*d*) PF = 84%   (*e*) $W = 1935$ W

JOB 19-8   **1.** 1310.8 kHz   **2.** 50 pF   **3.** 80 μH

JOB 20-1   **1.** 91.7%   **2.** (*a*) 99.6%   (*b*) 550 W   **3.** 536 W   **4.** (*a*) 50%   (*b*) 27 W   (*c*) 0.25 A   **5.** 0.7*a*   **6.** 2869 VA   **7.** 79,411 W

JOB 20-2   **1.** (*a*) 123.5 kW   (*b*) 110.2 kVA   (*c*) 74.3% lagging   (*d*) 166.2 kVA   **2.** (*a*) 70.7%   (*b*) 91 kVA   (*c*) 64 kW   **3.** (*a*) 57,102 VA   (*b*) 84.9%

JOB 20-3   **1.** (*a*) 44 kW   (*b*) 93.3% leading   (*c*) 47.159 kVA   (*d*) 214 A   **2.** (*a*) 12,320 W   (*b*) 12,644 VA   (*c*) 2839 var   (*d*) 97.4% lagging   (*e*) 57.5 A   **3.** (*a*) motor 1: true power 9964.8 W, apparent power 12456 VA, reactive power 7473.6 var, motor 2: true power 14 116.8 W, apparent power 16 608.0 VA, reactive power 8 802.2 var   (*b*) total true power 24 081.6 W, total reactive power 16 275.8 var, total apparent power 29 065.9 VA   (*c*) 83% lagging   (*d*) true power 6 747 W, apparent power 10 380 VA, reactive power 7 888.8 var   (*e*) true power 30 828.6 W, apparent power 31 949.1 VA, reactive power 8 387 var   (*f*) 96.5% lagging   (*g*) 76.95 A   **4.** (*a*) true power 600 kW, reactive power 528 kvar   (*b*) 89% lagging   (*c*) 107.91 A

JOB 20-4   **1.** 63.9%   **2.** (*a*) 72 kVA   (*b*) 41° lag   (*c*) 47.236 kvar   (*d*) One 15-kvar and one 25-kvar capacitors are needed to balance the lagging—47.236 kvar, leaving 7.236 kvar of reactive power   (*e*) 99.5%   **3.** *C* kilovars needed = 54.45 kvar, which would require three 25-*C* kvar capacitors

JOB 21-1   **1.** Three-phase equipment is smaller in size and more economical than single-phase equipment of the same power rating. For any particular size, horsepower ratings of three-phase motors and generators are greater than those of single-phase motors and generators. Three-phase motors are more efficient because power is more uniform (does not pulsate). Three-phase power distribution can be accomplished with only three-fourths of the copper line.   **2.** 762 V   **3.** 132.79 V   **4.** 80 A   **5.** 43.7 kW   **6.** (*a*) 2400 V   (*b*) 56 133 W   (*c*) 168.355 kW   **7.** (*a*) 90.499 kVA   (*b*) 83%   **8.** (*a*) 208 V   (*b*) 15 A   (*c*) 5.4 kVA   (*d*) 4136.4 W   **9.** 172 A

10. (*a*) 145 V   (*b*) 1.9 A   (*c*) 1.9 A   (*d*) 826 W   (*e*) 0.8275 kVA   **11.** (*a*) 7.3 Ω   (*b*) 62%   (*c*) 34.8 A   (*d*) 34.8 A   (*e*) 16.24 kW   (*f*) 26.489 kVA   **12.** (*a*) 11.418 kVA   (*b*) 10.276 kW

JOB 21-2   **1.** 77.9 A   **2.** (*a*) 8 000 V   (*b*) 735.25 A   (*c*) 10 200 kVA   (*d*) 8 160 kW   **3.** (*a*) 480 V   (*b*) 11.56 A   (*c*) 16.608 kVA   (*d*) 11.625 kW   **4.** (*a*) 14 Ω   (*b*) 0.857   (*c*) 25.7 A   (*d*) 44.5 A   (*e*) 23.75 kW   **5.** (*a*) 0.525   (*b*) 95.15 kVA   (*c*) 80.016 kvar   **6.** (*a*) 10 Ω   (*b*) 0.8 lag   (*c*) 208 V   (*d*) 20.8 A   (*e*) 35.98 A   (*f*) 10.357 kW   (*g*) 12.947 kVA   **7.** 550 V   **8.** (*a*) 8.9 A   (*b*) 5.14 A   **9.** (*a*) 131.4 A   (*b*) 440 V   (*c*) 33.33 kVA, 75.9 A, 440 V   **10.** (*a*) 302 A   (*b*) 175 A   (*c*) 235.107 kVA   **11.** (*a*) 56 kW, 42.13 kvar   (*b*) 29.33 kVA, 19.12 kvar   (*c*) 78 kW, 23 kvar   (*d*) 0.96   (*e*) 85.4 A

JOBS 22-1 AND 22-2
1. See Fig. 17.

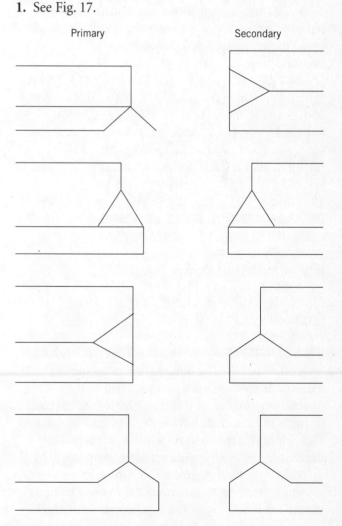

Primary   Secondary

2. See Fig. 18.

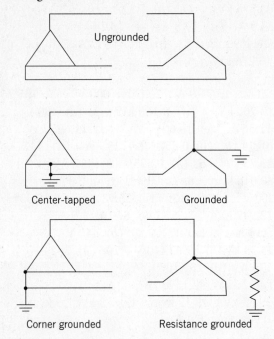

Ungrounded

Center-tapped   Grounded

Corner grounded   Resistance grounded

3. wye-delta connection   **4.** delta-wye connection
5. A delta connection allows one transformer to be removed from service while service is still provided on all three phases.   **6.** open-delta or V-connection   **7.** (*a*) 4 800 V   (*b*) 240 V
(*c*) 240 V   (*d*) 24 kVA   (*e*) 14.4 kW   (*f*) 2.89 A
(*g*) 57.8 A   (*h*) 5 A   (*i*) 13.872 kVA   (*j*) 41.616 kVA
8. (*a*) 120 V, 208 V   (*b*) 75 kVA   (*c*) 72 kVA
(*d*) 50.4 kW   (*e*) 72 kVA   (*f*) 4 160 V
(*g*) 10 A, 10 A   **9.** (*a*) 38.15 kV   (*b*) 4.8 kV
(*c*) 70 A, 40.5 A   (*d*) 581.3 kVA, 465 kW
(*e*) 465 kW   (*f*) 3 000 kVA   (*g*) 5.1 A
10. (*a*) 225 kVA   (*b*) 124.56 kVA   (*c*) 99.65 kW
(*d*) 240 V, 173.41 A   (*e*) 2 400 V, 30 A
(*f*) 2 400 V, 17.34 A   (*g*) 124.56 kVA

JOB 22-3   **1.** (*a*) 25.95 A   (*b*) 120 V
(*c*) 5 387.2 VA   (*d*) 15 A   (*e*) 120 V
(*f*) 3 114.0 VA   (*g*) 57.7%   **2.** (*a*) 60 kVA
(*b*) 34.68 kVA   (*c*) 10 A

JOBS 23-1 TO 23-6   **1.** switching circuits, digital logic circuits   **2.** The binary concept is simply that a device or gate can exist in one of two states, a HIGH or LOW, OFF and ON, or 0 and 1. A logic gate has one or more input signals but only one output signal. This concept is the basis on which circuits make decisions.   **3.** If all inputs are 1, the output will be 1. $S_1 \cdot S_2 = 1$.   **4.** $2^4 = 16$ combinations   **5.** six switches   **6.** The OR gate output is 1 if one or more inputs are 1. $S_1 + S_2 = 1$.   **7.** Computers use logic

gates to perform logical functions such as decisions, comparisons, arithmetic, and counting. Logic gates execute the basic operations of AND, OR, and NOT.   **8.** Many devices can be thought of as existing in one of two states. In logic circuits a HIGH input is referred to as a *closed switch* condition, and a LOW input is an *open switch* condition.   **9.** A truth table lists all the gate input combinations and the related output condition for each.   **10.** The NOT gate merely inverts binary numbers to their opposites. $\overline{S_1} = 1$.

11.

	Inputs		Output
S_1	S_2	S_3	L
0	0	0	0
0	0	1	0
0	1	0	0
0	1	1	0
1	0	0	0
1	0	1	0
1	1	0	0
1	1	1	1

$$S_1 \cdot S_2 \cdot S_3 = 1$$

12. The AND operation gives the logical product of two terms. The OR operation gives the logical sum of two terms. The NOT operation gives the logical negation (invert or complement) of a single term.

13.

	Inputs		Output
S_1	S_2	S_3	L
0	0	0	0
0	0	1	1
0	1	0	1
0	1	1	1
1	0	0	1
1	0	1	1
1	1	0	1
1	1	1	1

$$S_1 + S_2 + S_3 = L$$

14. See Fig. 19.

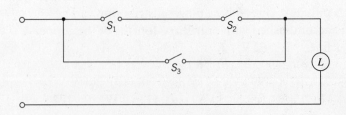

Inputs			Output
S_1	S_2	S_3	L
0	0	0	0
0	0	1	1
0	1	0	0
0	1	1	0
1	0	0	0
1	0	1	0
1	1	0	1
1	1	1	1

15. See Fig. 20.

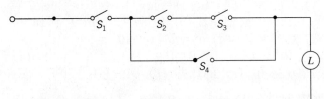

Inputs				Output
S_1	S_2	S_3	S_4	L
0	0	0	0	0
0	0	0	1	0
0	0	1	0	0
0	0	1	1	0
0	1	0	0	0
0	1	0	1	0
0	1	1	0	0
0	1	1	1	0
1	0	0	0	0
1	0	0	1	1
1	0	1	0	0
1	0	1	1	0
1	1	0	0	0
1	1	0	1	1
1	1	1	0	1
1	1	1	1	1

JOB 23-7

1.

Inputs				Output
S_1	S_2	S_3	S_4	L
0	0	0	0	1
0	0	0	1	1
0	0	1	0	1
0	0	1	1	1
0	1	0	0	1
0	1	0	1	1
0	1	1	0	1
0	1	1	1	1
1	0	0	0	1
1	0	0	1	1
1	0	1	0	1
1	0	1	1	1
1	1	0	0	0
1	1	0	1	0
1	1	1	0	1
1	1	1	1	0

2.

Inputs			Output
S_1	S_2	S_3	L
0	0	0	0
0	0	1	0
0	1	0	1
0	1	1	0
1	0	0	0
1	0	1	0
1	1	0	1
1	1	1	1

3.

Inputs			Output
S_3	S_2	S_1	L
0	0	0	1
0	0	1	0
0	1	0	1
0	1	1	0
1	0	0	0
1	0	1	0
1	1	0	0
1	1	1	1

JOBS 23-8 AND 23-9   **1.** (*a*) $R_m = S_1L_s\overline{OL}$
(*b*) $R_m = S_1L_s\overline{OL}R_m$ (*c*) $R_m = S_1L_s$
2. (*a*) $R_m = S_1F_1OLS_2$
(*b*) $R_m = S_1F_1\overline{OL}(S_2 + R_m)R_{m_1}$
(*c*) $R_m = S_1S_2OL$
3. See Fig. 21.

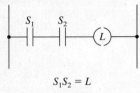

$$S_1S_2 = L$$

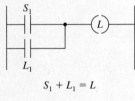

4. See Fig. 22.

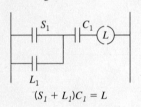

$$S_1 + L_1 = L$$

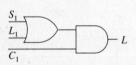

5. See Fig. 23.

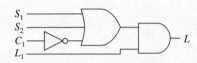

$$(S_1 + L_1)C_1 = L$$

Inputs			Output
S_1	L_1	C_1	L
0	0	0	0
0	0	1	0
0	1	0	0
0	1	1	1
1	0	0	0
1	0	1	1
1	1	0	0
1	1	1	1

$$(S_1 + L_1)C_1 = L$$

6. See Fig. 24.

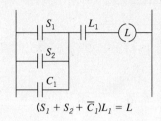

$$(S_1 + S_2 + \overline{C}_1)L_1 = L$$

JOB 24-1   **1.** (*a*) $3 = \log_7 1\,000$ (*b*) $5 = \log_2 423$
(*c*) $0.5 = \log_{15} 6$ (*d*) $0 = \log_4 1$ (*e*) $3 = \log_b 2$
(*f*) $2a = \log_3 M$ **2.** (*a*) $10^3 = 75$ (*b*) $2^5 = 180$
(*c*) $15^{0.6} = 7$ (*d*) $a^c = b$ (*e*) $10^3 = 50$
(*f*) $10^0 = 1$ **3.** (*a*) 1.7159   (*b*) 2.835   (*c*) 1.0149
(*d*) 0.5440   (*e*) 2.5185   (*f*) -2.7351

JOB 24-2 AND 24-3   **1.** 0.4 dB   **2.** 1 000   **3.** 40 dB
4. 14.39 dB   **5.** 0.0523 W   **6.** 24.4 dB   **7.** 12.97 dB
8. 13.50 dBm   **9.** 5.31 dB   **10.** 195.9 mA

JOB 24-4   **1.** 51.6 dB, 573.3 ft   **2.** 3.01 dB
3. 18.34 dB, 1.45 V   **4.** 114.6 ft   **5.** 6.49

Windows Test Generator Introduction

This Windows user's guide accompanies a test generator program called *ExamView Pro 2.0*—an application that enables you to quickly create printed tests, Internet tests, and computer-based tests. You can enter your own questions and customize the appearance of the tests you create. The *ExamView Pro* test generator program offers many unique features. Using the QuickTest wizard, for example, you are guided step-by-step through the process of building a test. Numerous options are included that allow you to customize the content and appearance of the tests you create.

As you work with the *ExamView Pro* test generator, you may use the following features:

- **an interview mode or "wizard" to guide you through the steps to create a test in less than five minutes**

- **five methods to select test questions**
  —from a list
  —random selection
  —by criteria (difficulty code or objective—if available)
  —while viewing questions
  —all questions

- **the capability to edit questions or to add an unlimited number of questions**

- **online (Internet-based) testing**
  —create a test that students can take on the Internet using a browser
  —receive instant feedback via e-mail
  —create online study guides with student feedback for incorrect responses
  —include any of the twelve (12) question types

- **online (computer-based) testing**
  —allow anyone or selected students to take a test
  —schedule tests
  —create online study guides with student feedback for incorrect responses
  —incorporate multimedia (movies and audio)
  —export student results to a gradebook or spreadsheet

- **a sophisticated word processor**
  —streamlined question entry with spell checker
  —tabs, fonts, and text styles
  —support for symbols and foreign characters
  —tables with borders and shading
  —full-featured equation editor
  —pictures or other graphics within a question, answer, or narrative

- **numerous test layout and printing options**
  —scramble the choices in multiple choice questions
  —organize matching questions in a one- or two-column format

—print multiple versions of the same test with corresponding answer keys

—print an answer key strip for easier test grading

—specify the layout of a test to conserve paper

—print a comprehensive answer sheet

- **link groups of questions to common narratives**

- **password protection**

- **extensive help system**

Installation and Startup Instructions

The *ExamView Pro* test generator software is provided on one or more floppy disks or on a CD-ROM depending on the question bank. The disks include the program and all of the questions for the corresponding textbook. The *ExamView Player,* which can be used by your students to take online (computerized) tests, is also included.

Before you can use the test generator, you must install it on your hard drive or network. The system requirements, installation instructions, and startup procedures are provided below.

System Requirements

To use the *ExamView Pro 2.0* test generator or the online test player, your computer must meet or exceed these minimum hardware requirements:

- 486, 66 MHz computer

- Windows 3.1, Windows 95, Windows 98, or Windows NT

- color monitor (VGA-compatible)

- high-density floppy disk drive

- hard drive with at least 5 MB space available

- 8 MB available memory *(16 MB memory recommended)*

- an Internet connection and access to a server are required for Internet testing features

- mouse

- printer

Installation Instructions

Follow these steps to install the *ExamView Pro* test generator software on a hard drive or network. The setup program will automatically install everything you need to use the *ExamView* software. **Note:** A separate test player setup program is also included for your convenience.

Step 1

Turn on your computer.

Step 2

Insert the *ExamView Pro* installation disk into Drive A. If the program is provided on a CD-ROM, insert the disk into your CD-ROM drive.

Step 3

Windows 3.1: While in the Program Manager, choose *Run* from the **File** menu.
Windows 95/98: Click the **Start** button on the *Taskbar* and choose the *Run* option.

Step 4

If you are installing the software from floppy disks, type **a:\setup** and press **Enter** to run the installation program. If the *ExamView Pro* software is provided on a CD-ROM, use the drive letter that corresponds to the CD-ROM drive on your computer (e.g., **d:\setup** or **d:\examview\setup**).

Note: The installation program is configured to copy the test generator software and the test player to *c:\examview* on your hard drive. You can, however, change this location. For example, you can select a location on your network server.

Step 5

Follow the prompts on the screen to complete the installation process. If the software and question banks are provided on more than one disk, you will be prompted to insert the appropriate disk when it is needed.

Step 6

Remove the installation disk from the disk drive when you finish.

Getting Started

After you complete the installation process, follow these instructions to start the *ExamView Pro* test generator software. This section also explains the options used to create a test and edit a question bank.

Startup Instructions

Step 1

Turn on the computer.

Step 2

Windows 3.1: Locate the *ExamView Pro* program icon. Double-click the program icon to start the test generator software.
Windows 95/98: Click the **Start** button on the *Taskbar*. Highlight the **Programs** menu and locate the *ExamView Pro* folder. Select the *ExamView Pro* option to start the software.

Step 3

The first time you run the software you will be prompted to enter your name, school/institution name, and city/state. You are now ready to begin using the *ExamView Pro* software.

Step 4

Each time you start *ExamView Pro,* the **Startup** menu appears. Choose one of the options shown in Figure 1 on page 38.

Step 5

Use *ExamView Pro* to create a printed, Internet, or LAN-based test. Or, edit questions in a new or existing question bank.

    ExamView Pro includes three components: Test Builder, Question Bank Editor, and Test Player. The **Test Builder** includes options to create, edit, print, and save tests. The **Question Bank Editor** lets you create or edit existing question banks. The **Test Player** is a separate program that your students can use to take online (computerized) tests.

    The Test Builder and the Question Bank Editor systems are integrated in one program. As you work with *ExamView Pro,* you can easily switch between the Test Builder and Question Bank Editor components using the *Switch to . . .* option in the **File** menu.

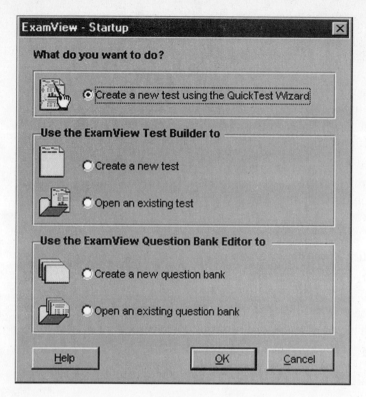

Figure 1 — ExamView Pro Startup Menu

Important: Whenever you need assistance using *ExamView Pro,* access the extensive help system. Click the **Help** button or choose an option from the **Help** menu to access step-by-step instructions. If you experience any difficulties while you are working with the software, you may want to review the troubleshooting tips in the user-friendly help system.

Test Builder

The Test Builder will empower you to create tests using the QuickTest Wizard or you can create a new test on your own. (See the sample test in Figure 2 on page 39.) Use the Test Builder to prepare both printed and online tests.

- *If you want ExamView Pro to choose questions randomly from one or more question banks,* choose the QuickTest Wizard option to create a new test. Then, follow the step-by-step instructions to (1) enter a test title, (2) choose the question bank from which to select questions, and (3) identify how many questions you want on the test. The QuickTest Wizard will automatically create a new test and use the Test Builder to display the test on screen. You can print the test as is, remove questions, add new questions, or edit any questions.

- *If you want to create a new test on your own,* choose the option to create a new test. Then identify a question bank from which to choose questions by using the *Question Bank* option in the **Select** menu. You may then add questions to the test by using one or more of the following selection options: *Randomly, From a List, While Viewing, By Criteria,* or *All Questions.*

You can customize the appearance of a test, edit test instructions, and choose to leave space for students to write their answers. When you print the test, you may choose how many copies of the test you want, whether you want all the

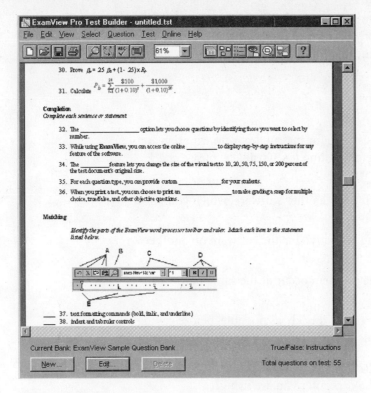

Figure 2 — Sample Test

copies to be the same, and whether you want to scramble the questions and the multiple choice options. If you choose to scramble the questions, *ExamView Pro* will print a custom answer sheet for each variation of the test.

If you want your students to take a test online, first create the test. Then, save the test as an Internet test/study guide or use the Online Test Wizard to create a test for delivery over a LAN (local area network). The software will walk you through the steps to turn any test into an online (Internet or LAN-based) test.

Question Bank Editor

The Question Bank Editor will empower you to edit questions in an existing publisher-supplied question bank or to create new question banks. Always use the Question Bank Editor if you want to change a question permanently in an existing question bank.

You may edit questions in a question bank or add new questions by using the built-in word processor. The word processor includes many features commonly found in commercially available word processing applications. These features include the following: fonts, styles, tables, paragraph formatting, ruler controls, tabs, indents, and justification.

A question bank may include up to 250 questions in a variety of formats including multiple choice, true/false, modified true/false, completion, yes/no, matching, problem, essay, short answer, case, and numeric response. You can assign a difficulty code, a page reference, and two objectives to each question.

Test Player

The Test Player is a separate program that lets your students take a test at a computer. Depending on the options you set, students can check their work themselves, receive feedback for incorrect responses, and print a detailed report. An online (LAN-based) test/study guide can include the following question types: Multiple Choice, True/False, Completion (Fill-in-the-Blank), Yes/No, Numeric Response, and Matching. You can also include multimedia elements (e.g., movies, animations, or audio).

Software Support

Glencoe provides toll-free telephone assistance for instructors who experience difficulty while using *ExamView Pro*. Before calling for assistance, please check the following:

- Is your computer working properly? Try some other software, which you know is working, on the same computer.
- Are you certain the software is working properly? Try the software on another computer.
- Can you repeat the problem? Does the problem occur at the same point each time?

In order for the Support Center to help you as quickly as possible, before calling for assistance have the following at hand:

- exact title and ISBN number from the disk label or package.
- brand, model, and configuration of the computer you are using.
- system version (Windows 3.1, Windows 95, or Windows 98) installed on your computer.
- the exact wording of any error message.

The Glencoe Support Center toll-free number is **800-437-3715.** The Support Center is available from 8:00 A.M. TO 6:00 P.M. Eastern Standard Time. You can also send an e-mail to the following address **epgtech@mcgraw-hill.com** to contact the Support Center.

Internet Activities

The Internet Activities, located on the Assessment page at the end of each chapter, are designed to give your students an opportunity to work on the Internet. By using the Internet to complete these activities, they will become more familiar with the Internet for use in school, work, and their personal lives.

Students can work independently or in groups to complete the Internet Activities. We suggest that you allow time in class for students to compare and discuss their answers with one another.

Also, you may want to have students search the Internet to find Web sites that would help them in their study of math for electricity and electronics. The Internet Activities are optional.

The sites referred to in the Glencoe Internet Activities are not under the control of Glencoe. Therefore, Glencoe can make no representation concerning the content of these sites. Extreme care has been taken to list only reputable links by using educational and government sites whenever possible. Internet searches have been used that return only sites that contained no content intended for mature audiences. Because sites change frequently, the sites referred to in the Internet Activities may no longer be available or may currently be under construction.

The sites listed below are for electricity and electronics and math help Web sites. These do not appear in the student edition, and so you may want to share them with your class or create projects for the students using these sites.

Internet Site	Organization
http://www.cemacity.org	CemaCity Home
http://www.forum.swarthmore.edu/students/	Swarthmore
http://www.nec.com	NEC
www.claussco.com	Clauss Electronics Division
www.cie-wc.edu	Cleveland Institute of Electronics
www.ceitron.com	Consolidated Electronics, Inc.
www.contact-east.com	Contact East, Inc.
www.controlledpwr.com	Controlled Power Co.
www.crowelec.com	Crow Electronics
www.dalco.com	Dalco Electronics
www.warnet/comsev_main.html	Dana Corp Warner Electric
www.daytaco.com	DAYTA-CO
www.tcp.co.uk/~diverse	Diverse Devices
www.panet/vcrtips	Electronic Software Developers
www.gen.com	Electronics Parts Supply
www.elect-spec.com	Electronic Specialists, Inc.
www.era.org	Electronics Representatives Association (ERA)
www.eta-sda.com	Electronic Technicians Association
www.electronix.com	Electronix Corporation
www.esi.com	Electroservice Laboratories
www.electrostandards.com	Electro Standards Lab, Inc.
www.mitechnologies.com	M.I. Technologies
www.mitsubishielectric.com	Mitsubishi Electric

Internet Site	Organization
www.moodytools.com	Moody Tools, Inc.
www.mot.com	Motorola
www.mouser.com	Mouser Electronics
www.multidyne.com	Multidyne Inc.
www.mztv.com	Museum of Television
www.mssystems.com	Music and Sound
www.neiparts.net	Nationwide Electronics
www.newportelect.com	Newport Electronics, Inc.
www.mhcec.com	NRI School of Electronics
www.orause.com	ORA Electronics
www.osha.gov	OSHA
www.paceuse.com	PACE, Inc.
www.ncl.net.au	Parker's Electronic Stuff Homepage—Australia
www.peaktech.com	The Peak Technologies Group
wwe.ecgproducts.com	Phillips ECG Company
www.philtek.com	Philtek Power Corp.
www.powersourceonline.com	PowerSource
www.powertronics.com	PowerTronics
www.galco.com	Galco Industrial Electronics
www.heathkit.com	Heathkit Educational Systems
hermanelectronics.com	Herman Electronics
www.hexaconelectric.com	Hexacon Electric Co.
www.spe.sony.com/pictures	High Definition Production
www.hi-techniques.com	Hi-Techniques, Inc.
www.ieib.com	International Electronics
www.intl-light.com	International Light, Inc.
www.iol.ie/ittdub	International Test Technologie
www.ittpomona.com	ITT Pomona Electronics
www.kalglo.com	Kalglo Electronics Co., Inc.
www.mcgsurge.com	MCG Electronics
www.mcmelectronics.com	MCM Electronics
www.hfac.uh.edu	Media Futures Archive
www.transmitter.com	Radio Frequency (RF)
www.cctvnet.com	Richardson Electronics
www.rselectronics.com	RS Electronics
www.hwsams.com	Howard W. Sams & Company
www.eta-sda.com	Satellite Dealers Association
http://oigsysop.atsc.allied.com	Satellite Situation Report
www.temic-rf.com	Satellite Tuners
www.sencore.com	Sencore Electronics
www.displaymate.com	Sonera Technologies
www.sony.com	Sony
www.sel.cony.com	Sony Service Company
www.specializedproducts.com	Specialized Products Company
www.syncpulse.com	SyncPulse Systems
www.synerget.com	Synergetix
www.systemsensor.com	System Sensor
www.team-systems.com	Team Systems, Inc.
www.techam.com	TechAmerica
www.toolsthatwork.com	Tech Assist, Inc.
www.mcenter.com/tips	Tech Info. Procurement Service

Electronics Figures Masters

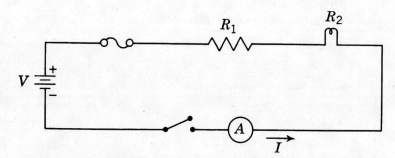

Figure 1-13

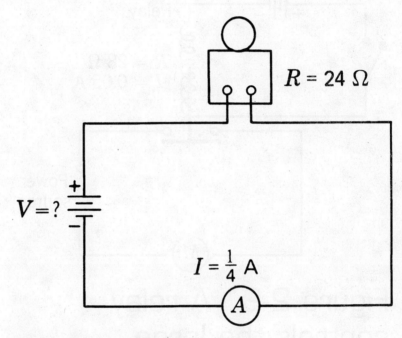

$R = 24 \, \Omega$

$V = ?$

$I = \frac{1}{4}$ A

Figure 2-8

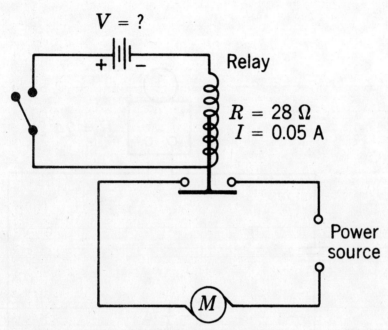

Figure 2-9   A relay controls the large current drawn by the motor.

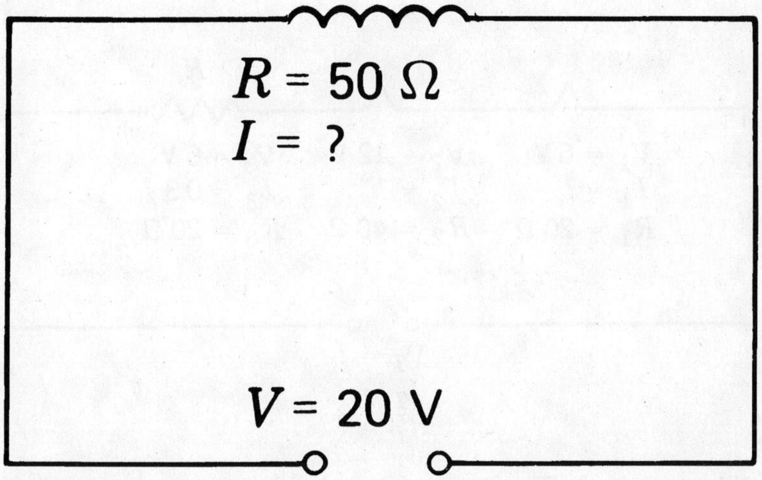

$R = 50\ \Omega$

$I = ?$

$V = 20\ V$

Figure 3-4

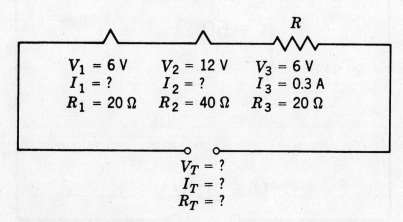

$V_1 = 6$ V $V_2 = 12$ V $V_3 = 6$ V
$I_1 = ?$ $I_2 = ?$ $I_3 = 0.3$ A
$R_1 = 20\ \Omega$ $R_2 = 40\ \Omega$ $R_3 = 20\ \Omega$

$V_T = ?$
$I_T = ?$
$R_T = ?$

Figure 4-5

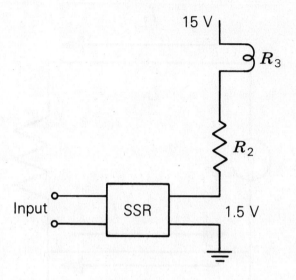

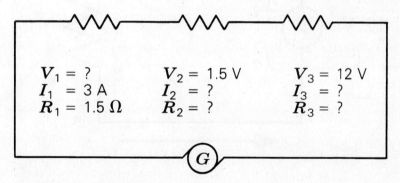

$V_1 = ?$ $V_2 = 1.5\ V$ $V_3 = 12\ V$
$I_1 = 3\ A$ $I_2 = ?$ $I_3 = ?$
$R_1 = 1.5\ \Omega$ $R_2 = ?$ $R_3 = ?$

Figure 4-8

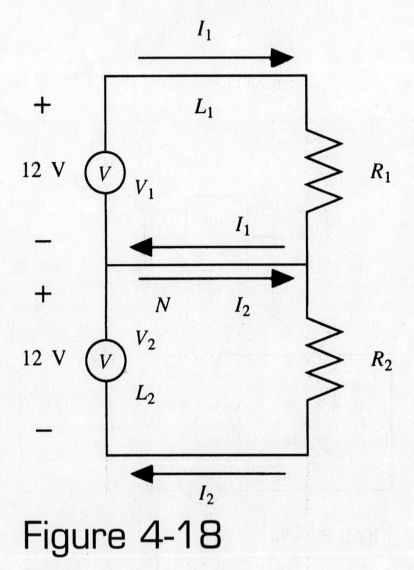

Figure 4-18

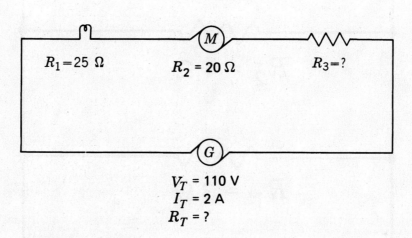

$R_1 = 25\ \Omega$

$R_2 = 20\ \Omega$

$R_3 = ?$

$V_T = 110$ V
$I_T = 2$ A
$R_T = ?$

Figure 4-24

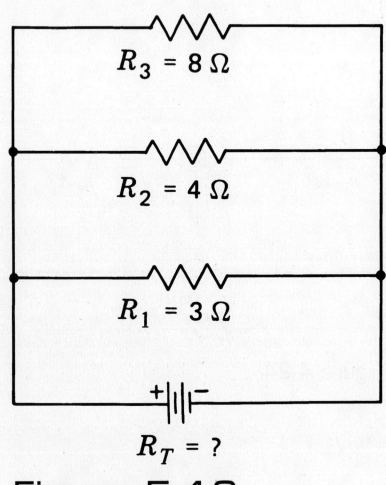

$R_3 = 8\ \Omega$

$R_2 = 4\ \Omega$

$R_1 = 3\ \Omega$

$R_T = ?$

Figure 5-18

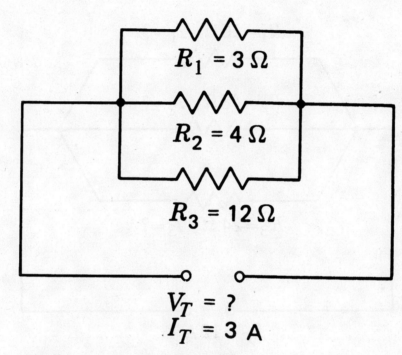

$R_1 = 3\,\Omega$

$R_2 = 4\,\Omega$

$R_3 = 12\,\Omega$

$V_T = ?$

$I_T = 3$ A

Figure 5-21

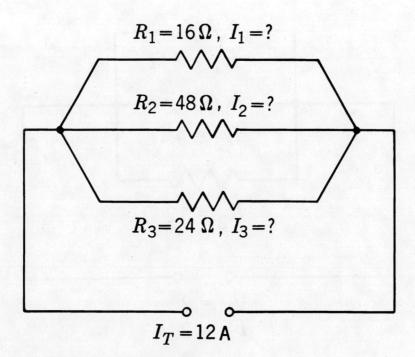

Figure 5-24

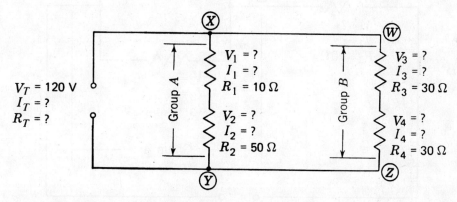

Figure 6-1 Parallel-series circuit.

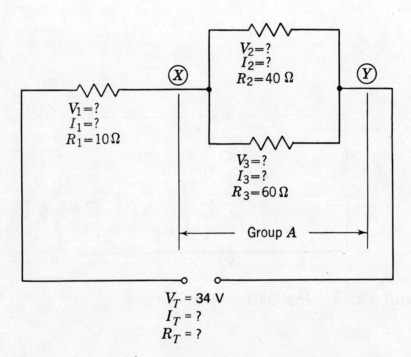

Figure 6-12   Series-parallel circuit.

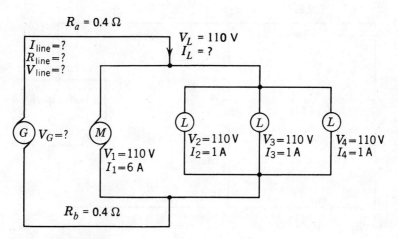

Figure 6-39

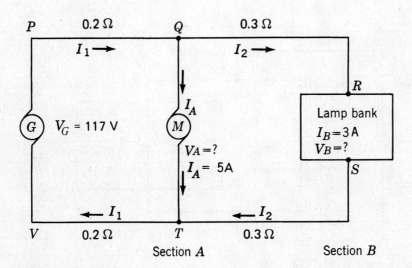

Figure 6-41

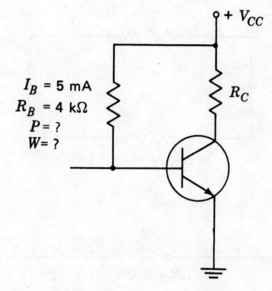

I_B = 5 mA
R_B = 4 kΩ
P = ?
W = ?

+ V_{CC}

R_C

Figure 7-4

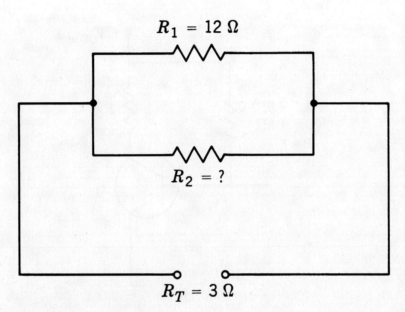

Figure 8-12

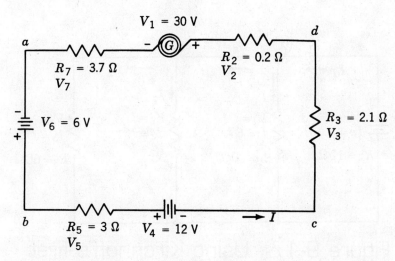

Figure 9-10 R_2 represents the internal
resistance of the generator.

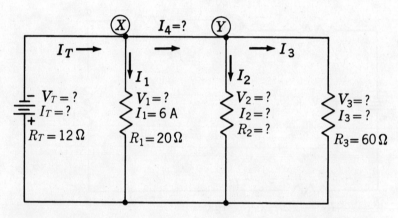

Figure 9-17   Using Kirchhoff's first law in parallel circuits.

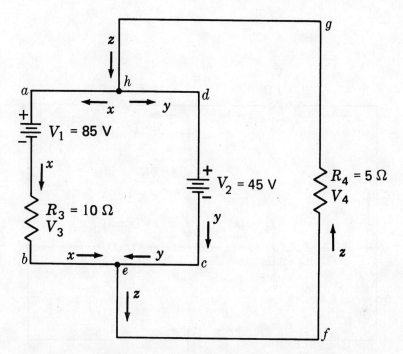

Figure 9-21   In complex circuits,
the branch currents are designat-
ed as *x, y,* and *z* A.

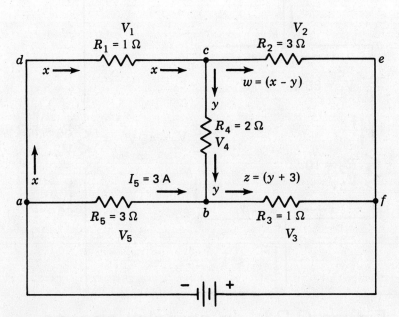

Figure 9-25

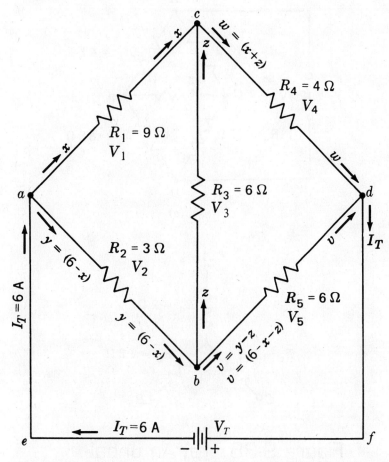

Figure 9-26 Unbalanced bridge circuit.

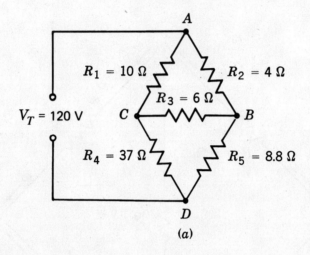

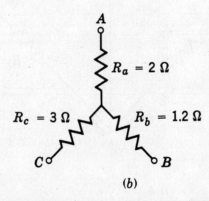

(b)

Figure 9-36 (a) An unbal-
anced bridge circuit. (b) The
Y equivalent of the delta circuit ABC.

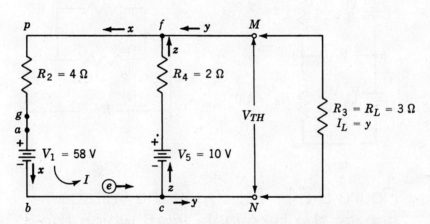

Figure 9-45 The circuit of Fig. 9-22 is redrawn to present only two terminals to the load.

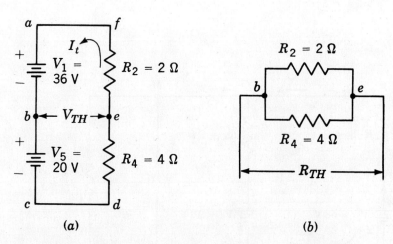

Figure 9-51 (a) V_{TH} is the voltage across the terminals from which the load has been removed. (b) The equivalent R_{TH} is the *total* resistance with all sources of emf shorted and the load removed.

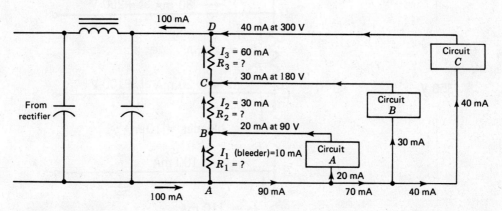

Figure 10-5

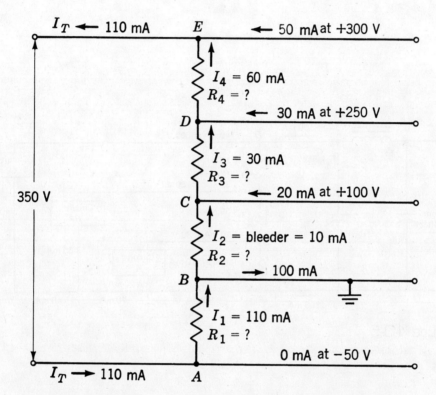

Figure 10-6   Voltage-divider circuit for
Self-Test 10-11.

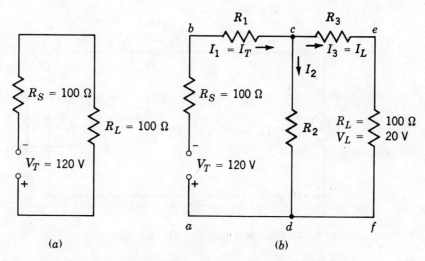

Figure 10-40 (a) Original circuit. (b) Circuit with T pad inserted; $R_1 = R_3$.

71

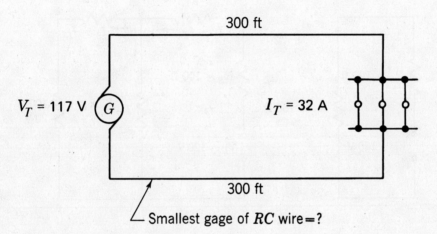

V_T = 117 V $\quad$ I_T = 32 A

300 ft

300 ft

Smallest gage of RC wire =?

Figure 13-1

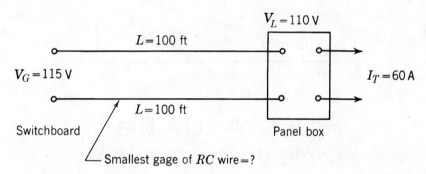

Figure 13-2

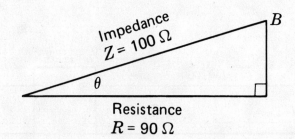

Figure 14-10   The
angle theta (θ) is the
phase angle in an
inductive ac circuit.

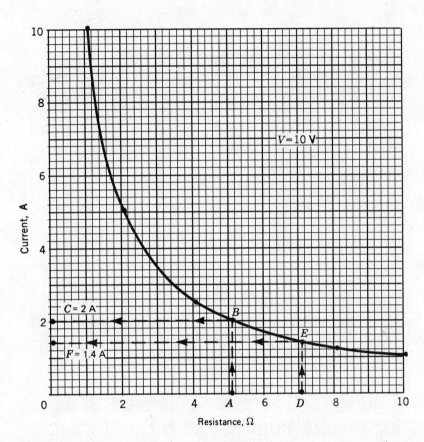

Figure 15-3 Relationship between current and resistance at a constant voltage.

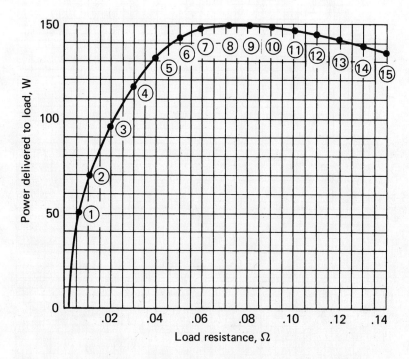

Figure 15-6 Power delivered to a
load plotted against load resistance.

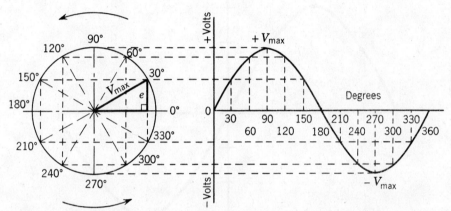

Figure 15-16   The voltage wave produced by a conductor rotating at a constant speed through a uniform magnetic field.

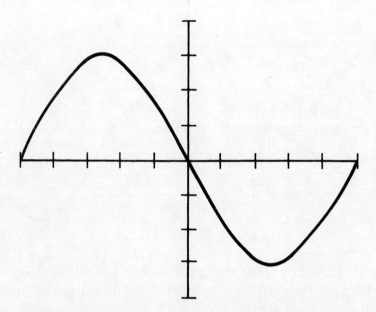

Figure 15-21 Sine wave displayed on an oscilloscope face.

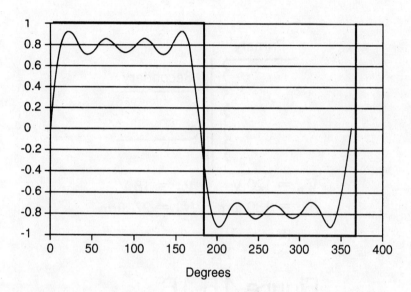

Figure 15-32

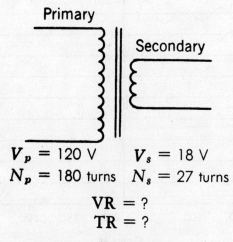

Figure 16-16

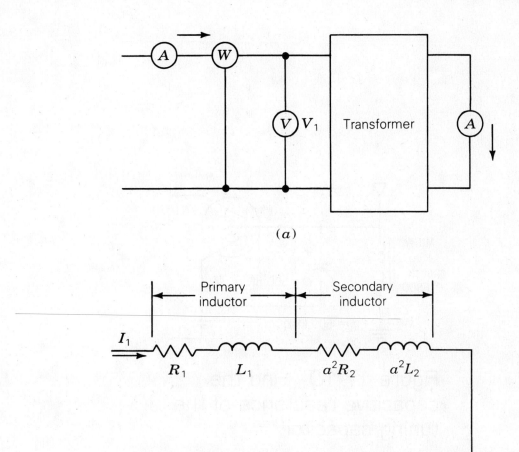

(a)

(b)

Figure 16-21 (a) Instrument setup for short-circuit test. (b) Model for short-circuit test.

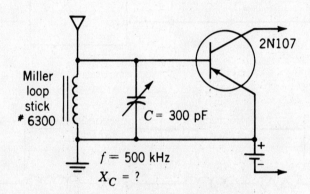

Figure 17-10   Find the capacitive reactance of the tuning capacitor.

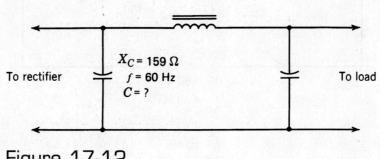

To rectifier

$X_C = 159\ \Omega$
$f = 60\ \text{Hz}$
$C = ?$

To load

Figure 17-12

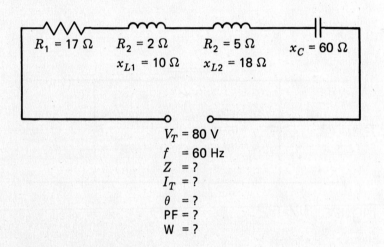

$$R_1 = 17\ \Omega \qquad R_2 = 2\ \Omega \qquad R_2 = 5\ \Omega \qquad x_C = 60\ \Omega$$
$$x_{L1} = 10\ \Omega \qquad x_{L2} = 18\ \Omega$$

$V_T = 80$ V
$f\ = 60$ Hz
$Z\ = ?$
$I_T = ?$
$\theta\ = ?$
PF $= ?$
W $= ?$

Figure 18-10

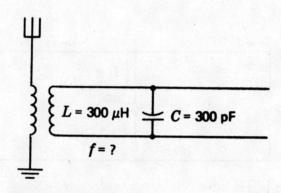

Figure 18-12

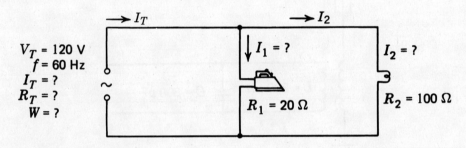

Figure 19-3

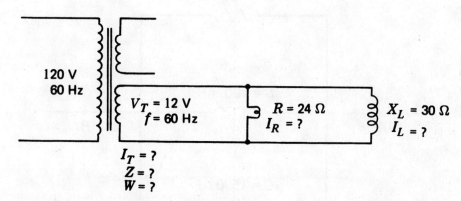

Figure 19-13   AC parallel circuit containing resistance and inductance.

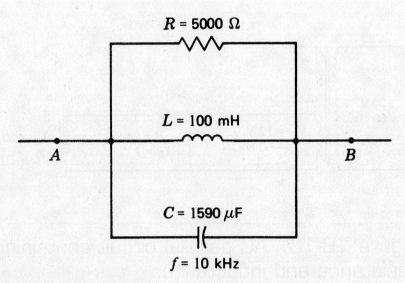

Figure 19-19

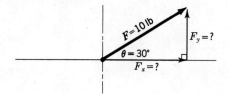

Figure 19-23

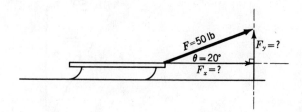

Figure 19-24

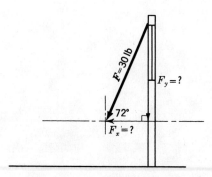

Figure 19-25 Only the vertical component of the force is effective in opening the window.

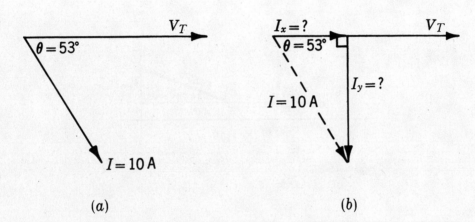

(a) (b)

Figure 19-27 (a) Phasor diagram for a lagging current. (b) The current I is resolved into its components I_x and I_y.

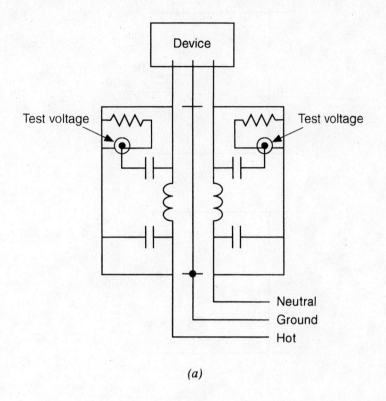

Device

Test voltage

Test voltage

Neutral

Ground

Hot

(a)

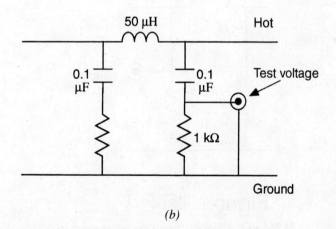

50 µH

Hot

0.1
µF

0.1
µF

Test voltage

1 kΩ

Ground

(b)

Figure 19-33   (*a*) FCC test
system. (*b*) Circuit values.

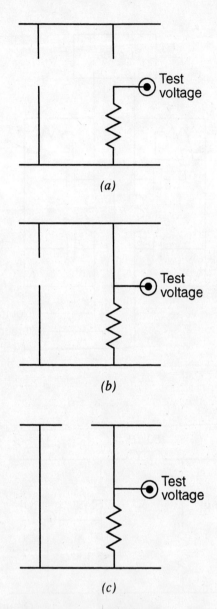

Figure 19-34
(*a*) Low frequencies.
(*b*) Mid-frequencies.
(*c*) High frequencies.

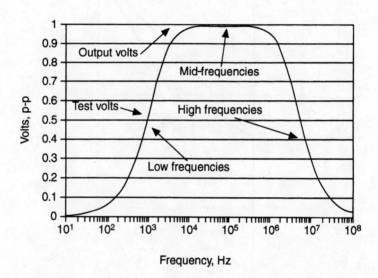

Figure 19-35   EMI test stand.

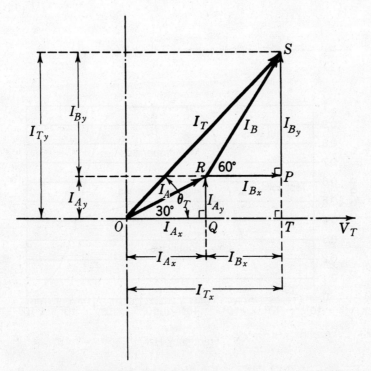

Figure 19-38 I_A and I_B have been resolved into their in-phase and reactive components. Their algebraic sums I_{T_x} and I_{T_y} are the components of the total current I_T.

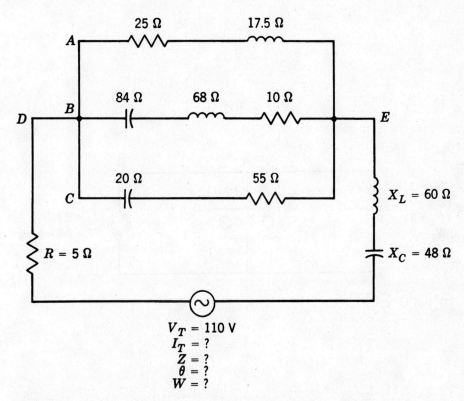

Figure 19-51   Series-parallel ac circuit.

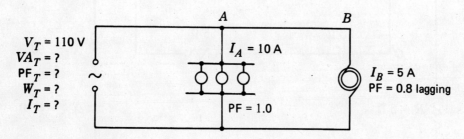

$V_T = 110\,\text{V}$
$VA_T = ?$
$PF_T = ?$
$W_T = ?$
$I_T = ?$

$I_A = 10\,\text{A}$

PF = 1.0

$I_B = 5\,\text{A}$
PF = 0.8 lagging

Figure 20-2

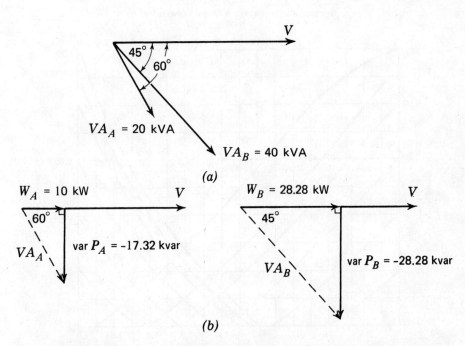

Figure 20-6   (a) VA_A and VA_B are not in phase, since they act at different power factors. (b) Resolution of each apparent power into its effective and reactive components.

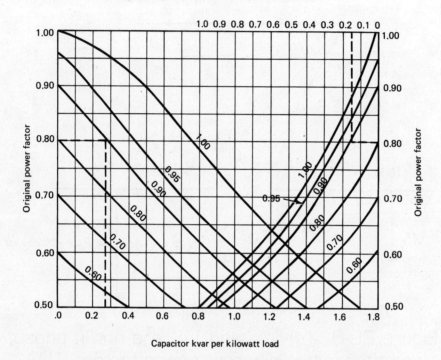

System capacity released—kVA per kilowatt load

Figure 20-23 Composite graph to determine (*a*) capacitor kvar required per kW load to improve PF, (*b*) system capacity released (kVA per kW load) for improved power factors.

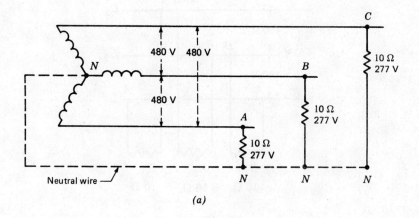

(a)

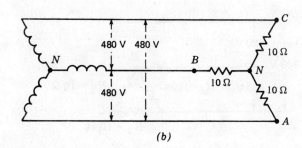

(b)

Figure 21-7

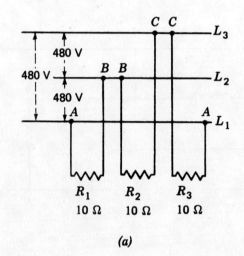

(a)

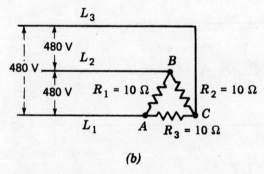

(b)

Figure 21-12

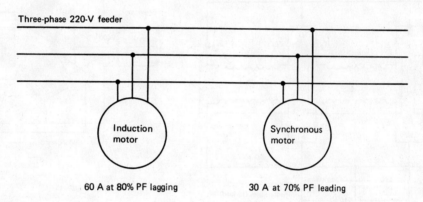

Three-phase 220-V feeder

Induction motor

Synchronous motor

60 A at 80% PF lagging

30 A at 70% PF leading

Figure 21-15

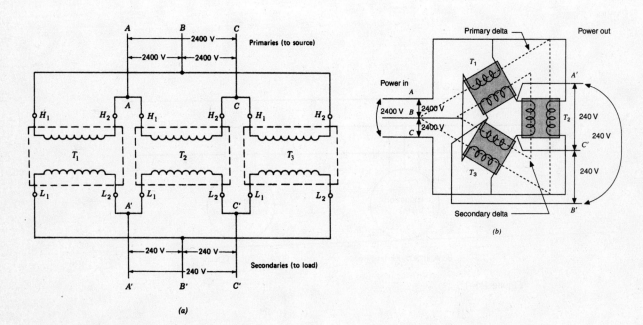

Figure 22-3 Connections for delta-delta. (*a*) Delta-delta connection for a three-phase 10:1 transformer. (*b*) Circuit in delta form.

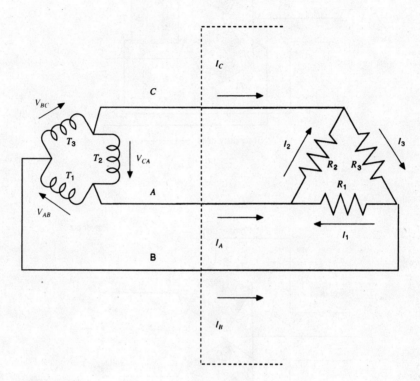

Figure 22-5

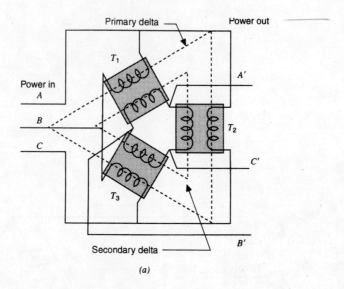

(a)

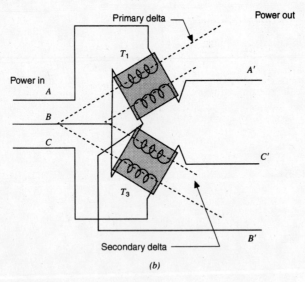

(b)

Figure 22-10

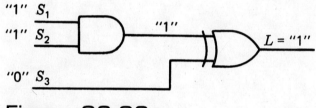

Figure 23-23